MATHEMATICS FOR INTRODUCTORY SCIENCE COURSES: CALCULUS AND VECTORS

MATHEMATICS
FOR
INTRODUCTORY
SCIENCE
COURSES:

W. A. BENJAMIN, INC.   *New York, Amsterdam*   1965

Daniel A. Greenberg

Columbia University

CALCULUS AND VECTORS

With a review of algebra, analytic geometry, and trigonometry

MATHEMATICS FOR INTRODUCTORY SCIENCE COURSES: CALCULUS AND VECTORS—With a Review of Algebra, Analytic Geometry, and Trigonometry

Library of Congress Catalog Card Number 65–17012
Manufactured in the United States of America

The manuscript was put into production on December 9, 1964; this volume was published on May 21, 1965

W. A. BENJAMIN, INC.
New York, New York   10016

to

H. S. G.

PREFACE

The purpose of this book is to make generally accessible the basic mathematical knowledge and techniques needed in the natural and physical sciences. The emphasis throughout the book is on the intuitive—and, where possible, pictorial—understanding of the material, rather than on formal presentation. I have used this approach because it is my conviction that no branch of mathematics is without an intuitive foundation, known to and used by professional mathematicians as well as teachers and students.

As will be emphasized in the text, it is not my intention to belittle the rigorous presentations of this material in currently available standard textbooks. On the contrary, my wish is to provide the reader with the tools and insights that will make it possible for him to read such books and to overcome his fear of their formal, often forbidding, aspect. There is *no substitute* for carefully done mathematics, presented in accordance with the highest standards of rigor, esthetics, and accuracy known today. There is, however, a *precursor* to such mathematics, and it is the lack of such precursors in published form that I have set out to fill.

This book is primarily designed to cover the needs of introductory courses and contains most of the material required to this end. In particular, much of the book is devoted to an elementary exposition of calculus, which furnishes the simplest and most useful means for achieving an understanding of the laws of nature.

The aim throughout has been to write in the simplest language possible and to provide a profusion of exercises and examples so that the beginner will at every point be convinced that the material is well within his reach. In the words of Oliver Heaviside, "We cannot all be Newtons or Laplaces, but that there is an immense amount of moderate mathematical talent lying latent in the average man I regard as a fact."[1] To the reader possessing considerable mathematical training, the book may serve as a reminder of the easily grasped intuitive ideas that lie at the root of presentday achievements.

Daniel A. Greenberg

New York, New York
August 1964

---

[1] O. Heaviside, *Electromagnetic Theory* (New York: Dover, 1950), p. 2, paragraph 8.

ACKNOWLEDGMENTS

This manuscript has benefited greatly from numerous discussions with Professor Robert Fuller and from his careful critique. Professor Fuller was also kind enough to use the manuscript in a "trial run" with his class, a procedure which netted many useful pointers of pedagogic value. To the members of the class, too, a debt of thanks for their cooperation is owed.

As with almost all my work, this has been reviewed and criticized by Mr. Dennis Flynn. Nothing goes through his hands that is not improved by the passage. Mr. David Landau has also been of great help with his detailed remarks. Of course, none of those who have helped improve this manuscript are responsible for its point of view, its contents, and its structure.

To Miss Charlotte Pearlberg I owe my special thanks for preparing a typescript of exceptional beauty and accuracy; and to Mr. John Landstreet, for helping me prepare the art work.

CONTENTS

MATHEMATICS FOR INTRODUCTORY SCIENCE COURSES: CALCULUS AND VECTORS

PART I

REVIEW OF ELEMENTARY MATHEMATICS

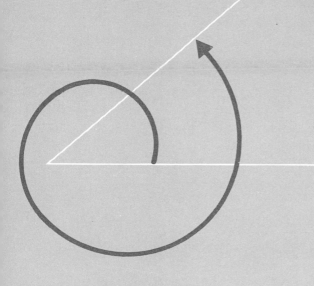

INTRODUCTORY
NOTE

Anyone who sets out to study science today must know certain basic elements of mathematics. These basic elements are taught to virtually everyone in high school, and we shall assume that they have been studied by the reader at one time or another. However, since frequently many years elapse between the study of mathematics and the study of science, and since there exists today no universally accepted curriculum or notation in mathematics, we shall summarize in Part I all the fundamental mathematical information that will be required for what follows. Except for a few instances, where experience has shown that most people have difficulty the first time they study the material, we shall limit ourselves to the barest summary of the material and shall refer the reader to standard texts for further explanation and enlightenment. Much of the content of Part I is extremely simple, but we have preferred to include even elementary facts and formulas in order to avoid unpleasant surprises for the reader in later chapters.

We shall assume that everyone knows and is at home with the elements of arithmetic, including the basic properties of the natural numbers, integers, fractions, rational and irrational numbers, and the real number system as a whole.[1]

[1] We shall have no occasion to make direct use of set theory or of the foundations of mathematics as presented in up-to-date mathematics courses. Perhaps the best comprehensive survey of mathematics written in a lucid and readable style from a modern point of view is R. Courant, and H. Robbins, *What is Mathematics?* (4th ed., New York: Oxford, 1960). This book is a valuable addition to any library and affords pleasure to the casual reader, who enjoys "dipping into" a book, as well as to the serious student. Chapter headings include "The Natural Numbers," "The Number System of Mathematics," "Geometrical Constructions," "The Algebra of Number Fields," "Projective Geometry. Axiomatics. Non-Euclidean Geometries," "Topology," "Functions and Limits," "Maxima and Minima," and "The Calculus." In the words of the authors, the book was written "for beginners and scholars, for students and teachers, for philosophers and engineers, for classrooms and libraries" (Preface to the First Edition). It attempts "to proceed on a straight road from the very elements to vantage points from which the substance and driving force of modern mathematics can be surveyed" (*ibid.*); the attempt is for the most part successful.

1

GEOMETRY[1]

1. CONGRUENCE AND SIMILARITY

Two figures are said to be *congruent* if one can be superimposed exactly on the other, i.e., if they are identical in *form* and *size*, and two figures are said to be *similar* if they have the same shape but differ by a scale factor, i.e., if they are identical in *form* only, but not identical in size (Fig. 1-1). For example, all circles are similar, since they all have the same shape, but only circles with equal radii are congruent, since only circles with equal radii can be superimposed exactly on one another.

Two triangles are congruent ($\cong$) if all the corresponding sides are the same length and all the corresponding angles the

---

[1] For further details, see any standard text in elementary geometry, such as *Plane Geometry for Colleges* by L. J. Adams (New York: Holt, Rinehart & Winston, 1958).

same size. This will be true if two angles and the included side of one are equal to two angles and the included side of the other, or if two sides and the included angle of one equal two sides and the included angle of the other, or if three sides of one equal three of the other.

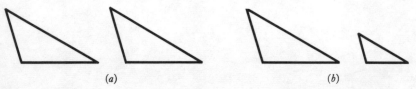

(a)   (b)

Fig. 1-1   (a) Congruence. (b) Similarity.

Two triangles are similar ($\sim$) if all the corresponding angles are the same size. This will be true if two angles of one equal two angles of the other (because then, in fact, all three angles of one equal all three of the other), or if two sides of one triangle stand in the same proportion to the two corresponding sides of the other and the included angles are equal, or if three sides of one triangle stand in the same proportion to the three corresponding sides of the other.

2. ANGLES

An angle (usually represented by a Greek letter, e.g., α) is defined by the spread between two lines (or *sides*) that come together at a point (the *vertex* of the angle).

Two angles, α and β, defined, respectively, by sides AA', AA'', and BB', BB'' are equal if their sides are mutually perpendicular (i.e., if AA' is perpendicular to ($\perp$) BB' and $AA'' \perp BB''$). See Fig. 1-2.

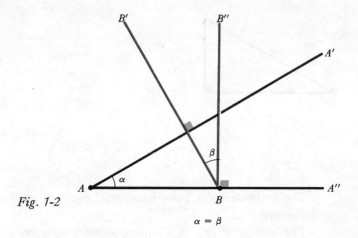

Fig. 1-2

$\alpha = \beta$

The sum of the angles in a triangle is 180°. An external angle of a triangle is equal to the sum of the opposite interior angles (see Fig. 1-3). For more on angles, see Chapter 4, Section 1.

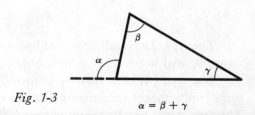

Fig. 1-3

$\alpha = \beta + \gamma$

3. PYTHAGORAS' THEOREM

The sum of the squares of the sides of a right triangle is equal to the square of the hypotenuse of the triangle (see Fig. 1-4).[2]

---

[2] For a discussion of some of the many proofs given throughout history for this theorem, see *The Thirteen Books of Euclid's Elements*, trans. and comm. by T. L. Heath (New York: Dover, 1956), Vol. 1, pp. 350–366.

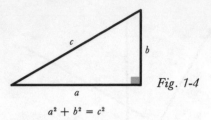

Fig. 1-4

$$a^2 + b^2 = c^2$$

4. PERIMETERS

The perimeter of a two-dimensional figure is the length of its boundary.

The perimeter (p) of a square a units long on a side is $p = 4a$ units of length. The perimeter of a rectangle of width w and length l is $p = 2w + 2l = 2(w + l)$.

The perimeter of a circle of radius r is $2\pi r$.

5. AREAS

The area of a two-dimensional figure is the number of square units required to cover the figure entirely.

The area (A) of a square a units long on a side is $A = a^2$ square units; that of a rectangle of width w and length l is $A = wl$. The area A of a parallelogram of base b and height h is $A = bh$ (see Fig. 1-5).

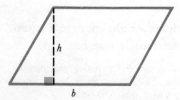

Fig. 1-5

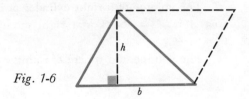

Fig. 1-6

The area of a triangle of base b and height h is $A = (\frac{1}{2})bh$ (Fig. 1-6).

The area of a circle of radius r is $A = \pi r^2$.

The surface area of the sides of a right cylinder (i.e., a cylinder whose sides are $\perp$ its base, see Fig. 1-7) of height h and base perimeter p is $A = ph$. (For the special case of a right circu-

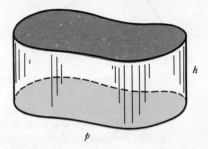

Fig. 1-7

lar cylinder, $A = 2\pi rh$.) The total surface area of a cylinder is the sum of the area of the sides and the area of the top and bottom.

The area of the surface of a sphere of radius r is $A = 4\pi r^2$.

6. VOLUMES

The volume of a three-dimensional figure is the number of cubic units required to fill the figure entirely.

The volume (V) of a rectangular parallelepiped of width w, length l, and height h is $V = wlh$ cubic units. For a cube a units long on a side, $V = a^3$.

The volume of a right cylinder of height h having a base of area A is $V = Ah$. For a right circular cylinder of radius r, $V = \pi r^2 h$.

The volume of a sphere of radius r is $V = (\frac{4}{3})\pi r^3$.

EXERCISES

1. There are three right triangles in Fig. 1-8: $\triangle ABC$, $\triangle ABD$, $\triangle BCD$. Are any two of these congruent? Are any two similar?

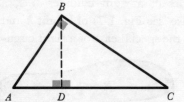

Fig. 1-8

2. Are all ellipses similar? all rectangles? all slices of pie? Are all squares congruent?
3. An isosceles triangle is a triangle with two equal sides and with two equal angles opposite these sides. Prove that all isosceles right triangles are similar. Are *all* isosceles triangles similar?
4. Can a triangle have two right angles?
5. Given a right triangle as shown in Fig. 1-9, determine the values of β corresponding to the following values of α: $\alpha = 30°$, $45°$, $60°$, $64°$, $78°$.

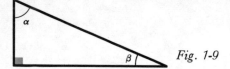

Fig. 1-9

6. Is the hypotenuse of a right triangle *always* bigger than either of the sides?
7. A 10 ft ladder is leaned against a vertical wall so that its top is 8 ft above the ground. The bottom of the ladder is kicked by a passer-by,

moving it 2 ft further from the wall. How much does the top of the ladder descend?

8. A square of side a has perimeter $4a$, and area a^2. A rectangle whose width is $(\frac{1}{2})a$ and whose length is $(2a)$—constructed by cutting the square in half and joining the ends—has the same area

$$A = (\tfrac{1}{2})a \cdot (2a) = a^2$$

but larger perimeter ($p = 5a$). Why? Where does the "extra" perimeter come from?

9. Consider a circle of diameter a and a square of side a. Which can be inscribed in the other? What is the ratio of the perimeters? of the areas? Is there anything surprising about the answer?

10. What is the area of a square whose diagonal is d units long?

11. What happens to the area of a rectangle if its height is doubled? tripled?

12. If the radius of a circle is doubled, by how much is the area increased? What if the radius is tripled?

13. If the radius of a sphere is doubled, by how much is the surface area increased? the volume? What if the radius is tripled?

14. What is the smallest number of water tanks of radius 20 ft that will hold at least as much water as a water tank of radius 50 ft? (All the tanks are assumed to have the same height.)

2

ALGEBRA[1]

1. VARIABLES

A fundamental entity in algebra is the *variable*, a quantity whose numerical value is not specified. Variables are designated by letters, usually chosen (by convention) from the end of the alphabet: e.g., x, y, z, etc. (Known numbers are usually symbolized by letters chosen from the beginning of the alphabet: e.g., a, b, c, etc.) Variables play a central role in algebra, because algebra deals with the solution of problems in which the numerical value of some unknown quantity is determined by a set of conditions. For example, consider the following often-used sample of an algebraic problem: "If pencils are sold two for a dime, what is the price of one pencil?" Here, the unknown is the price of a

[1] For further details, see any standard text in algebra, such as *College Algebra* by Moses Richardson (Englewood Cliffs: Prentice-Hall, 1958).

single pencil; the condition that determines the value of the unknown is the given price of two pencils. Algebraic techniques are generally applicable to such problems, whether they occur in the realm of business, economics, sociology, natural science, or anything else. In the case of science, the unknowns are always quantities that somehow measure physical phenomena; the conditions that determine the values of these quantities are either the laws of nature or some set of specifications particular to the problem at hand.

Algebra provides the means for solving such problems, and the foremost of these means is the replacement of the *words* in the problem by *symbols*. In particular, the first step in the solution of an algebraic problem is to designate the unknowns by letters. (For example, in the case of the problem mentioned earlier: "Let *x* stand for the price of one pencil.") Using these symbols, the conditions can be translated into equations involving the unknowns ("$2x = 10$"), and the equations can then be solved with the aid of general techniques applicable to the solutions of problems arising in any field.

2. ONE VARIABLE

A *monomial* is an expression made up of a variable raised to some power, multiplied by a numerical coefficient (e.g., $5x$, or ax^3). A *polynomial* is an expression consisting of the sum or difference of two or more monomials.

A *linear expression in one variable* (or a *polynomial of the first degree*) is an expression in which the variable is raised to the first power and no higher (e.g., $ax + b$). A *linear equation* can be formed by setting a linear expression equal to zero:

$$ax + b = 0 \tag{2-1}$$

This is the simplest type of algebraic equation, and its solution is

$$x = -(b/a) \qquad (2\text{-}2)$$

A *quadratic expression in one variable* (or a *polynomial of the second degree*) is an expression in which the variable is raised to the second power and no higher (e.g., $5x^2 + 2$; $ax^2 + bx + c$). A quadratic equation in one variable results when a quadratic expression is set equal to zero:

$$ax^2 + bx + c = 0 \qquad (2\text{-}3)$$

The solutions of this equation can be found and are:

$$x = \frac{-b \pm \sqrt{b^2 - 4ac}}{2a} \qquad (2\text{-}4)$$

There are two unequal (real) solutions when $b^2 > 4ac$; when $b^2 = 4ac$, the two solutions are equal (a *double root*); when $b^2 < 4ac$, the two solutions have imaginary parts (see Section 7).

Generally speaking, a *polynomial of the nth degree* is an expression in which the variable is raised to the nth power and no higher. An equation of the nth degree is an equation formed by setting a polynomial of nth degree equal to zero.

When two or more polynomials are multiplied together, the product is the sum of all the monomials obtained by multiplying each term in one polynomial by each term in the other polynomial, term by term. This can be done most easily using the format of long multiplication. Thus, the product $(x + 6)(3x^2 + 4x + 5)$ can be found as follows:

$$
\begin{array}{r}
3x^2 + 4x + 5 \\
x + 6 \\
\hline
3x^3 + 4x^2 + 5x \\
+ 18x^2 + 24x + 30 \\
\hline
3x^3 + 22x^2 + 29x + 30
\end{array}
$$

In other words $(x + 6)(3x^2 + 4x + 5) = 3x^3 + 22x^2 + 29x + 30$.

Often a polynomial can be written as the product of two or more polynomials (or as the product of a monomial and a polynomial). When the polynomial is so written, it is said to be *factored*. Occasionally, polynomials can be factored at sight; for example, it can be seen immediately that $5x^2 + 15x + 25$ can be written $5(x^2 + 3x + 5)$ or that $6x^3 + x$ can be written $x(6x^2 + 1)$. Usually, some ingenuity or insight is required to factor a polynomial; for example, it is not immediately evident that $x^2 + 17x + 72$ can be written $(x + 8)(x + 9)$. Whenever a factored polynomial is encountered, the reader can check the factoring by multiplying together the factors and seeing that they give the original polynomial. [Thus, the product of $(x + 8)$ and $(x + 9)$ is found to be $x^2 + 17x + 72$, and this shows the stated factoring to be correct.] Three types of polynomial are encountered so frequently that their factors are worth noting. The first is the perfect square:

$$x^2 + 2ax + a^2 = (x + a)(x + a) = (x + a)^2 \qquad (2\text{-}5)$$

[E.g., $x^2 + 10x + 25 = (x + 5)^2$.] The second is the difference of squares:

$$x^2 - a^2 = (x - a)(x + a) \qquad (2\text{-}6)$$

[E.g., $x^2 - 25 = (x + 5)(x - 5)$,

or $x^2 - 7 = (x + \sqrt{7})(x - \sqrt{7})$.]

The third is slightly more general: it is the difference of nth powers, and in this case it is important to know that such an expression always has the difference of the *first* powers as a factor:

$$x^n - a^n = (x - a)(\text{polynomial of } [n - 1]\text{th degree}) \qquad (2\text{-}7)$$

Equation 2-6 is seen to be the simplest example of Eq. 2-7.

3. MORE THAN ONE VARIABLE. FUNCTIONS

Frequently, two or more unknowns appear in a problem. In such cases, in order to be able to determine the numerical values of these unknown quantities, we must have as many different equations (i.e., as many conditions) as there are unknowns; in other words, to obtain a complete solution of the problem we must have one equation per unknown. If we have fewer equations than unknowns, then we can determine only as many of the unknowns (in terms of the others) as there are equations.

In a problem involving two or more variables, the problem itself (i.e., the conditions set forth in the problem) specifies relations between the values of the variables. For example, consider a problem in two variables (x, y) where we are told that the value of y is always twice the value of x. This statement links all the values of x and y in such a way that whenever x is known, y can also be determined. *Whenever two variables* (e.g., x, y) *are linked in such a way that the value of one* (e.g., y) *is determined when the value of the other* (x) *is given, we say that the former is a "function" of the latter* ("y is a function of x"). The properties described in the statement linking the latter variable to the former (in our example, the property "twice as big as x," i.e., "$2x$") are called "the function" ("the function of x"); they are represented by a general symbol, such as "$f(x)$," "$g(x)$," "$h(x)$" (pronounced "f of x," "g of x," "h of x," respectively). Thus, in general, two variables linked by some statement are said to be related by a functional relationship, and this is expressed symbolically by an equation such as "$y = f(x)$," or "$u = g(w)$." These definitions are illustrated by the following example. Consider the statement, "The total cost of a research project is twice the direct expenses, plus \$1,000." This statement links two variables, the total cost ($\equiv y$, where the symbol "$\equiv$" stands for "is identical to" or "is defined as") and the direct expenses ($\equiv x$); we are told that, in dollars, y is always twice x plus 1,000. Because y and x are linked in such a way that the value of y is determined whenever the value of x is given, we say that y is a function of x $[y = f(x)]$. From the particular statement given, we can see that the particular function of x with which we are dealing is $2x + 1,000$ ("twice x plus 1,000"), so that, in symbols, we have $y = f(x) = 2x + 1,000$.

The terminology illustrated above for two variables can be extended to any number of variables. Whenever a relation exists among variables such that the value of one of them is determined when the values of the others are specified, we say that that variable is a function of the other variables; and the particular function involved is found directly from the relation. For example, suppose we say that the total charge for utilities ($\equiv u$) is the sum of the charge for gas ($\equiv v$) and the charge for electricity ($\equiv w$). The mere fact that the charge for utilities is determined by the charge for gas and for electricity tells us that u is a function of v and w $[u = f(v, w)]$. The particular statement of how u is determined from v and w (i.e., the statement "the sum of the charge for gas and the charge for electricity") tells us the particular form of the function in this case, viz., $u = f(v, w) = v + w$.

This terminology is useful and convenient: it enables us to speak generally about relations between variables and to derive theorems and make assertions generally valid for *all* such relations. Thus, theorems that begin with the words "Suppose we have a function of x" or "Suppose y is a function of x" will apply generally to *all* functions of x, or to *all* functional relationships between y and x; they will not be limited to particular functions (e.g., $3x$, $5x^2$, $7x + 5$, etc.) or to particular relations (e.g., $y = 5x + 2$, $y = 7x^2$, etc.). Indeed, the transition from the study of *particular* functions to the study of properties of *functions in general* contributed much to the spectacular progress made in mathematics during the last three centuries.

4. EXPONENTS (POWERS)

A number a raised to a positive integral power $n \geq 1$ (written a^n; the number a is called the *base*) is defined to be the repeated product $a \cdot a \cdot a \cdot \ldots \cdot a$, where a appears n times. (Note that $a^1 = a$ according to this definition.) By applying the definition directly, we find that $a^2 a^3 = a^5$, and, in general, $a^n a^m = a^{n+m}$. This is the basic rule for multiplication with exponents: The *product* of two numbers, each of which consists of the same base raised to some integral positive power, is the base raised to the *sum* of the powers of the factors.

We can extend the rule to division, the inverse of multiplication. Consider the following: $a^7/a^3 = a^4 (= a^{7-3})$; $a^3/a^7 = 1/a^4 (= 1/a^{7-3})$. In general, $a^n/a^m = a^{n-m}$ when $n > m$, and $a^n/a^m = 1/a^{m-n}$ when $m > n$. Now, both these statements can be combined into a single rule identical to the rule for products if we introduce the simple convention that *a base raised to a negative integral power is by definition the inverse of the base raised to the positive integral power:*

$$a^{-m} \equiv 1/a^m \tag{2-8}$$

Using Eq. 2-8, we see that both statements for division reduce to the multiplication rule $a^n a^{-m} = a^{n-m}$ where n, m are positive integers, $n \neq m$; or, more generally, $a^n a^m = a^{n+m}$, where n, m are positive or negative integers, $n \neq -m$. In the case where $m = -n$, we have $a^n a^{-n} = a^n/a^n = 1$. If we agreed that the multiplication rule should apply to this case too, we would have $1 = a^n a^{-n} = a^0$. The convention is therefore adopted that

$$a^0 \equiv 1, \tag{2-9}$$

i.e., any base raised to the zero power is unity; this allows us to drop the restrictions on m, n, so that m and n can be arbitrary whole numbers, positive, negative, or zero.

Consider, now, the root $\sqrt{a}$. From the definition of the square root we know that $\sqrt{a}\sqrt{a} = a = a^1$. If we naïvely wrote

$\sqrt{a}$ in the form of a base raised to a power u, i.e., if we set $\sqrt{a} = a^u$, we would have $a^u a^u = a^1$. Applying the law of multiplication, we would find $2u = 1$, or $u = \frac{1}{2}$. Similarly, since $\sqrt[3]{a}\, \sqrt[3]{a}\, \sqrt[3]{a} = a^1$, if we set $\sqrt[3]{a} = a^v$, we would find $v = \frac{1}{3}$; and, in general, if we set $\sqrt[n]{a} = a^z$, we would find $z = 1/n$. We see, then, that if we adopt the convention

$$\sqrt[n]{a} = a^{1/n} \tag{2-10}$$

we can extend the use of powers to numbers that are *roots*, by the simple expedient of introducing fractional exponents. The ordinary rules of multiplication will then apply to fractional exponents too.

When a base raised to a power is itself raised to a power [e.g., when we form $(a^3)^2 = a^3 a^3 = a^6$, or $(a^{\frac{1}{3}})^3 = a^{\frac{1}{3}} a^{\frac{1}{3}} a^{\frac{1}{3}} = a^1$], the result can be summarized in the law

$$(a^n)^m = a^{nm} \tag{2-11}$$

which holds for n, m as positive or negative whole numbers, zero, or fractional powers of the form $1/z$. Using Eq. 2-11, we can introduce arbitrary rational exponents, since we have, for example, $a^{\frac{2}{3}} = (a^2)^{\frac{1}{3}} = \sqrt[3]{(a^2)} = (a^{\frac{1}{3}})^2 = (\sqrt[3]{a})^2$; and, in general, $a^{q/r} = (a^q)^{1/r} = (a^{1/r})^q$. Our use of powers has thus been extended to arbitrary rational exponents, and both Eq. 2-11 and the basic law of multiplication

$$a^m a^n = a^{m+n} \tag{2-12}$$

hold for arbitrary rational m, n (positive, negative, or zero). In fact, once these laws have been extended to all rational numbers, they can be extended to arbitrary real numbers (rational or irrational).[2]

[2] See, for example, K. Knopp, *Theory and Application of Infinite Series* (4th ed., New York: Hafner, 1947), pp. 49–57. The first chapter of this book (pp. 3–43) gives an excellent introduction to the fundamentals of the theory of real numbers.

5. LOGARITHMS

Let

$$a^n = b \tag{2-13}$$

(We shall restrict ourselves to values of a greater than 1.) We call n "the logarithm of b, to the base a"; the logarithm of the number b to the base a is thus the power to which a must be raised to give b:

$$n = \log_a b \tag{2-14}$$

One of the most common bases in use is the base 10; this base is often convenient, since we commonly employ the decimal system of numbers (a number system based on ten fundamental numerical units). If we use the base 10, certain logarithms—namely, integral logarithms—are readily accessible, as the following table shows:

Since $10^0 = 1$,   we know that $\log_{10} 1$ $= 0$
" $10^1 = 10$,   " $\log_{10} 10$ $= 1$
" $10^2 = 100$,   " $\log_{10} 100$ $= 2$
" $10^3 = 1{,}000$,   " $\log_{10} 1{,}000 = 3$
etc.

And since $10^{-1} = 1/10$,   we know that $\log_{10} 0.1$ $= -1$
" $10^{-2} = 1/100$,   " $\log_{10} 0.01$ $= -2$
" $10^{-3} = 1/1{,}000$,   " $\log_{10} 0.001 = -3$
etc.

All intermediate numbers have intermediate (nonintegral) logarithms. For example, the logarithm of any number between 10 and 100 lies between 1 and 2; the logarithm of any number between 1 and 10 lies between 0 and 1; and so forth.

Suppose we have another number c, such that

$$a^m = c, \quad m = \log_a c \tag{2-15}$$

Then, since $bc = a^n a^m = a^{n+m}$ by Eq. 2-12, we see that

$$\log_a (bc) = n + m = \log_a b + \log_a c \qquad (2\text{-}16)$$

by Eqs. 2-14 and 2-15; the logarithm of a product is thus the sum of the logarithms of the factors.[3] Equation 2-16 holds for all logarithms, positive or negative, just as Eq. 2-12 holds for all powers, positive or negative. Thus, for example, since $b/c = a^n/a^m = a^{n-m}$, we have

$$\log_a (b/c) = n - m = \log_a b - \log_a c \qquad (2\text{-}17)$$

The basic law for logarithms, Eq. 2-16, makes it possible to construct tables of logarithms as follows. Consider the number 2358. This can be written $2.358 \times 1000 = 2.358 \times 10^3$. Then by Eq. 2-16 $\log_{10} 2358 = \log_{10} 2.358 + \log_{10} 10^3 = \log_{10} 2.358 + 3$. Or consider the number 0.000764. This can be written 7.64×10^{-4}, so that

$$\log_{10} 0.000764 = \log_{10} 7.64 + (-4)$$

In similar fashion, any (positive) number can be written as the product of a number lying between 1 and 10 (whose logarithm lies between 0 and 1) and a power of 10 (whose logarithm can be found by examination). For this reason, the tables give only the logarithms of numbers between 1 and 10, and these suffice to determine the logarithm of any number.

Some properties of the logarithmic function $\log_a b = n$ deserve special notice. (1) Since $a^0 = 1$ for all a, $\log_a 1 = 0$ for all a; i.e., the logarithm of 1 to any base is zero. (2) Since we have assumed $a > 1$, we have $a^n > 1$ for all $n > 0$ (all powers—even fractional powers—of a number greater than 1 are themselves greater than 1). Thus, $a^n = b > 1$ for $n > 0$, so that $\log_a b > 0$

---

[3] Products can therefore be converted into sums by the use of logarithms. This fact is the principle on which the slide rule is based; see, for example, W. E. Breckenridge, *The Polyphase Slide Rule* (Hoboken and New York: Keuffel and Esser, 1944), especially Chapter II (pp. 19–32).

for $b > 1$; i.e., the logarithm (to any base) of a number greater than 1 is positive. (3) When n is negative ($n < 0$), $a^n = a^{-|n|} = 1/a^{|n|}$ is greater than zero and smaller than 1 (since $a^{|n|}$ is greater than 1, and the inverse of a number greater than 1 is always smaller than 1). Thus, for $n < 0$, $a^n = b < 1$, so that $\log_a b < 0$ for $b < 1$; i.e., the logarithm (to any base) of a positive number smaller than 1 is negative. (4) According to (3), as $b = a^n = 1/a^{-|n|}$ gets smaller, $|n|$ must get larger, so that n gets more negative. We can summarize this with the statement that as b approaches zero (as $b \rightarrow 0$), n becomes more negative ($n = \log_a b \rightarrow -\infty$). (5) No power n (whether positive, negative, or zero) can make a^n negative. Thus, if the number b is negative, it cannot be written in the form a^n. In other words, the logarithm cannot be defined for negative numbers.[4]

Consider, now, the number b^m. By Eqs. 2-13 and 2-11:

$$b^m = (a^n)^m = a^{nm} \tag{2-18}$$

so that, by Eq. 2-14,

$$\log_a (b^m) = nm = m(\log_a b) \tag{2-19}$$

Thus, the logarithm (to any base) of a number raised to the power m is m times the logarithm of the number.

Suppose we have two different bases, a and e. In terms of these bases, we have (by the definition of a logarithm, Eq. 2-14)

$$a^n = b \rightarrow n = \log_a b \tag{2-20}$$
$$e^p = b \rightarrow p = \log_e b \tag{2-21}$$

We would like to find the relation between n and p—that is, we would like to know how the logarithm changes with change of base. *The key to finding this relation is to express one base in terms of the*

---

[4] This statement is valid as long as we restrict ourselves to logarithms that are real numbers. If we introduce logarithms that are complex numbers (see Section 7), we can extend the definition of $\log_a b$ to include $b < 0$. We do not discuss this extension to $b < 0$, since we shall not require it.

other. We know that for some q,

$$e^q = a \rightarrow q = \log_e a \qquad (2\text{-}22)$$

This means that $b = a^n$ can be written

$$b = a^n = (e^q)^n = e^{qn} \qquad \log_e b = qn \qquad (2\text{-}23)$$

Comparing Eqs. 2-23 and 2-21, we see that the desired relation is $p = qn$, or, by Eqs. 2-20, 2-21, and 2-22:

$$\log_e b = (\log_e a)(\log_a b) \qquad (2\text{-}24)$$

6. PROGRESSIONS

1. A series of numbers a_0, a_1, a_2, a_3, . . . is called an *arithmetic progression* if each term differs from the one just before it by the same amount d. Thus, in an arithmetic progression, if the first term is the number c, the second term will be $c + d$, the third term $c + 2d$, and so forth:

Term	a_0	a_1	a_2	a_3	. . .
Value	c	$c + d$	$c + 2d$	$c + 3d$	. . .

The sum of the terms from a_0 to a_n (the first $n + 1$ terms) is:

$$a_0 + a_1 + a_2 + \ldots + a_n = (n + 1)c + \frac{n(n + 1)d}{2}$$

$$(2\text{-}25)$$

The left-hand side of this equation can be written more concisely if we introduce the *summation symbol* $\sum_{j=n}^{N}$ (capital sigma, with "running index" j), which means "the sum of the terms obtained by letting j take on all integral values between the lower value n and the upper value N"; i.e.,

$$\sum_{j=n}^{N} a_j \equiv a_n + a_{n+1} + \ldots + a_N \qquad (2\text{-}26)$$

With the aid of Eq. 2-26, we can write Eq. 2-25 as:

$$\sum_{j=0}^{n} a_j = \sum_{j=0}^{n} (c + jd) = (n + 1)c + \frac{n(n + 1)d}{2} \quad (2\text{-}27)$$

2. A series of numbers a_0, a_1, . . . is called a *geometric progression* if each term is equal to the product of the one just before it and a fixed number r. (We restrict ourselves to cases where $r \neq 1$, so that the terms actually differ from one another.) Thus, in a geometric progression, if the first term is the number c, the second term will be cr, the third term cr^2, and so forth:

Term a_0 a_1 a_2 a_3 . . .
Value c cr cr^2 cr^3 . . .

The sum of the terms from a_0 to a_n is:

$$\sum_{j=0}^{n} a_j = \sum_{j=0}^{n} cr^j = \frac{c(1 - r^{n+1})}{1 - r}, \, r \neq 1 \quad (2\text{-}28)$$

Note that if $|r| < 1$, then $|r^2| < |r|$, $|r^3| < |r^2|$, $|r^4| < |r^3|$, and, in general, $|r^p|$ gets smaller ($|r^p| \rightarrow 0$) as p gets larger (as $p \rightarrow \infty$). For $|r| < 1$, then, even an *infinite* geometric progression has a definite sum:

$$\sum_{j=0}^{\infty} a^j = \sum_{j=0}^{\infty} cr^j = \frac{c}{1 - r}, \, |r| < 1 \quad (2\text{-}29)$$

7. IMAGINARY AND COMPLEX NUMBERS

In the course of solving algebraic problems, we often encounter the square root of a negative number. This occurs, for example, when we are seeking the solutions of a quadratic equation for which $b^2 < 4ac$ (see Eq. 2-4). The square root of a negative number cannot be a real number, since the rules of multiplication require that the square of any real number, positive or negative, be positive. The square root of a negative number must therefore lie outside the domain of real numbers. To this end, a simple notation is introduced, based on the fact that for any positive number a, we can write

$$\sqrt{-a} = \sqrt{(-1)(a)} = \sqrt{a}\sqrt{-1} \qquad (2\text{-}30)$$

so that the square root of any negative number can be written as the product of the square root of a positive number (which is a real number) and the square root of -1. We introduce the notation

$$\sqrt{-1} \equiv i \qquad (2\text{-}31)$$

This notation makes it clear that $\sqrt{-1}$ is not a real number. In terms of i, Eq. 2-30 becomes

$$\sqrt{-a} = \sqrt{a}\,i = ci, \text{ where } c = \sqrt{a} \qquad (2\text{-}32)$$

Such numbers are called "imaginary numbers," and i is called "the imaginary unit" (since all imaginary numbers are multiples of i). The sum or difference of imaginary numbers is also imaginary:

$$\sqrt{-a} \pm \sqrt{-b} = \sqrt{a}\,i \pm \sqrt{b}\,i = (\sqrt{a} \pm \sqrt{b})i \qquad (2\text{-}33)$$

Products of imaginary numbers can be evaluated with the aid of the following multiplication table:

$$
\begin{aligned}
i^1 &= i \\
i^2 &= i \cdot i = -1 \\
i^3 &= i \cdot i^2 = -i \\
i^4 &= i^2 \cdot i^2 = +1 \qquad (2\text{-}34)
\end{aligned}
$$

Since $i^4 = 1$, the powers of i from 5 to 8 simply repeat the powers from 1 to 4, i.e., $i^5 = i^4 \cdot i = 1 \cdot i = i^1$; $i^6 = i^4 \cdot i^2 = 1 \cdot i^2 = i^2$; $i^7 = i^3$; $i^8 = i^4$) as do the powers from 9 to 12, and so forth. From Eq. 2-34 we see that products of imaginary numbers may or may not be imaginary.

We can generalize further to the notion of a *complex number*, which is the sum of a real number and an imaginary number (i.e., which is made up of the two kinds of number we have at our disposal):

$$c = a + bi \qquad (a, b \text{ real}) \tag{2-35}$$

The sum of two complex numbers is complex:

$$\begin{aligned} c_1 + c_2 &= (a_1 + b_1 i) + (a_2 + b_2 i) \\ &= (a_1 + a_2) + (b_1 + b_2)i \end{aligned} \tag{2-36}$$

The product of two complex numbers is also complex, since, from Eq. 2-34, we find that

$$\begin{aligned} c_1 c_2 &= (a_1 + b_1 i)(a_2 + b_2 i) \\ &= a_1 a_2 + a_1 b_2 i + a_2 b_1 i + b_1 b_2 i^2 \\ &= (a_1 a_2 - b_1 b_2) + (a_1 b_2 + a_2 b_1)i \end{aligned} \tag{2-37}$$

Note that we do not restrict the values of a, b to any special range; they may be positive, negative, or zero. In the special case where $a = 0$, we are dealing with complex numbers that have only an imaginary part ("pure imaginary complex numbers"); and when $b = 0$, we are dealing with complex numbers that have only a real part. In other words, complex numbers include real numbers and imaginary numbers as special subsets.

The number obtained from c by changing the sign of the imaginary part of c is called "the complex conjugate (c.c.) of c," and is denoted by c^*. Thus, if $c = a + bi$, then

$$c^* \equiv a - bi \tag{2-38}$$

The c.c. is important because

$$c \cdot c^* = (a + bi)(a - bi) = a^2 + b^2 \qquad (2\text{-}39)$$

that is, because a number c multiplied by its c.c. is a pure real number, which is the sum of the squares of the numerical magnitudes of the real and imaginary parts of c.

8. PROPORTIONALITY

We say that one quantity y is proportional to a second quantity x when a *relative change* in x always leads to the same *relative change* in y—e.g., when doubling x doubles y, tripling x triples y, etc. The expression "y is proportional to x" is denoted by:

$$y \propto x$$

Since the definition of proportionality requires that the relative changes in x and y always be the same, the ratio y/x must remain constant when $y \propto x$; this is because multiplying x by 2 or 3 or any number n multiplies y by 2 or 3 or n, respectively, so that the ratio y/x remains unaffected. Thus, when $y \propto x$, $y/x = k$ (where k is some constant):

$$y \propto x \leftrightarrow y = kx \qquad (k \text{ is a constant}) \qquad (2\text{-}40)$$

The particular value of k depends on the particular conditions of the problem. Note the difference between proportionality and linearity: When we say that y varies linearly with x, it means that $y = ax + b$; when we say that y is proportional to x, it means that $y = ax$. Proportionality is thus a special case of linearity—one for which the constant term b vanishes.[5]

---

[5] In terms of the graph of the relationship between y and x (see Chapter 3, Section 4), proportionality implies that this graph is a straight line whose y-intercept is zero (i.e., a straight line passing through the origin).

9. PHYSICAL UNITS (DIMENSIONS[6])

The unknowns in a problem may be either pure numbers (as in the problem, "What is the number whose cube is 64?") or physical quantities (as in the problem, "If two pencils cost 10 cents, what is the price of one pencil?"). In the latter case, one must be careful always to bear in mind, and to write explicitly, the physical units in terms of which the unknown is measured ("Let x = the price of one pencil, in *cents*"). (Basic physical units are also called *dimensions*.) In particular, whenever an equation is written containing unknowns, the units on both sides of the equation must be the same, since *equality* can hold only between things of the same kind. Otherwise, the equation makes no sense. For example, no number of *cents* can ever be *equal* to a number of *pencils*.

When unknowns are multiplied in an equation, the units of the product are the product of the units of the individual factors. For example, if the solution of a problem calls for multiplying a variable representing the *number of men* involved, by a variable representing the *number of hours* they work, the product has the units. *man-hours*, and anything to which this product is set equal must also have the units *man-hours*. Similarly, when variables are divided, the quotient has units equal to the quotient of the units of the numerator and denominator. For example, if a problem calls for dividing the *number of pounds* consumed by the *number of people* doing the consuming, the quotient has units *pounds per person* (also written *pounds/person*). If the numerator and denominator have the *same* dimensions, the quotient is a pure number (since the dimensions cancel out). Thus, in calculating the cost-of-living index, a quotient is formed of the cost of living, in dollars,

---

[6] The use of the word "dimension" in this section is to be distinguished from its use in geometry. The two uses are quite different and need never be confused because the contexts in which they are used always serve to indicate the sense intended.

today, divided by the cost of living, in dollars, in some particular year chosen as standard, and the resulting quotient (the index) turns out to be a pure number.

In general, since the choice of units always involves an arbitrary convention specifying the size of the basic unit, any variable having dimensions is itself completely arbitrary in numerical magnitude. This is because the numerical magnitude of the variable would be different if we chose another set of units. (A problem whose solution is $x = \$1$ would have a solution of different numerical magnitude if we chose French francs as the unit, namely, $x = 5$ new francs.) On the other hand, variables that are dimensionless—i.e., that are pure numbers, whether by specification or by virtue of the fact that they represent quotients of quantities having the same dimensions—have numerical magnitudes that are *independent* of the choice of units used. (The cost-of-living index will be the same whether the cost of living is calculated in dollars, cents, francs, or wampum beads.) Such *dimensionless quantities* are always preferred, since they reflect magnitudes of fundamental, rather than accidental, significance.

In science, as elsewhere, dimensional analysis plays an important role. On the one hand, study of the dimensions involved in a problem makes it possible for us to be sure our equations are properly balanced with respect to units. On the other hand, this study helps us find, where possible, combinations of variables (products and quotients) that are dimensionless and hence independent of arbitrary conventions.

EXERCISES

1. Multiply the following: $(x - 3)(x + 2)$; $(x^2 - 6x + 4)(x + 5)$; $(x + 13)(x - 13)$; $(x^2 - 9)(x^2 + 3x - 2)$.
2. Factor the following: $3x^2 + 5x$; $4x^3 - 2x + 6$; $4x^3 - 3x^2 + 6x$; $12x^3 - 4x$; $x^2 - 16$; $x^2 + 8x + 16$.

3. Factor the expression $(a^{\frac{3}{2}} - b^{\frac{3}{2}})$.

4. Which of the following factorings are correct: $8x^2 - 10x - 18 = (4x - 9)(2x + 2)$; $x^2 + 6x + 9 = (x + 3)^2$; $x^2 - 6x - 9 = (x - 3)^2$; $x^2 - 25 = (x + 5)(x - 5)$; $x^2 + 25 = (x + 5)(x + 5)$.

5. Given the quadratic equation $ax^2 + 4x + 1 = 0$, what must a be in order for the two solutions to be equal? Can you factor the equation for this value of a?

6. A rectangle of perimeter 48 cm is twice as long as it is wide. What is its width?

7. The product of two consecutive positive integers is 240. What is the first integer?

8. A father is now twice as old as his son. Seventeen years ago the father was three times as old as his son. How old is the father now?

9. The sum of four consecutive positive integers is 46. What is the first integer?

10. In 1927 Charles Lindbergh flew from New York to Paris at an average speed of 107.4 miles per hour (mi/hr). Eleven years later, Howard Hughes flew the same route at an average speed of 217.1 mi/hr, in 16 hr and 57 min less time than it took Lindbergh. How many miles long was the New York-to-Paris route used by these fliers?

11. Express the area (A) of a rectangle as a function of its length (l) and width (w). If we are dealing with rectangles which are always three times as long as they are wide, what is A a function of? What function?

12. What is the functional relationship between the hypotenuse of a right triangle and the sides? What about the case of an isosceles right triangle?

13. What do you think automobile insurance rates are a function of? What about life insurance rates? Can you say anything, in words, about the nature of these two functions?

14. If $f(x) = x^3 - 3$, find $\dfrac{f(x) - f(-x)}{f(x) + f(-x)}$.

15. Find the value of $f(x + a)$ when $f(x)$ is: $x - 3$; x^2; $2x^2 + 5$; $x^3 + x$.

16. Given $f(u) = u + 3$, $g(v) = v^3 - 4$, find $g[f(u)]$.

17. Given $f(x) = \dfrac{1 - x}{1 + x}$, show that $f[f(x)] = x$.

18. Solve the following two equations for x and y:

$$y = 9 + 3x - 2x^2$$
$$y + x - 3 = 0$$

19. Express the following roots as (fractional) exponents: $\sqrt[3]{a}$; $\sqrt[7]{a^5}$; $\sqrt[5]{a}$; $\sqrt[4]{a^3}$. Find the following products: $\sqrt[7]{a^5} \cdot \sqrt[4]{a^3}$; $\sqrt[3]{a} \cdot \sqrt[5]{a}$.

20. Which of the following are correct: $5 \cdot 5^2 = 5^3$; $5^3 \cdot 25^2 = 5^7$; $8 \cdot 2^2 = 2^5$; $2^3 \cdot 2^7 = 2^{21}$; $6^5/6^3 = 6^2$; $6^5/3^2 = 2^3$; $6^5/3^5 = 2^5$.

21. What are the values of: $(7)^0$; $(\frac{1}{10})^{-1}$; $(\frac{1}{4})^{-\frac{1}{2}}$; $(\frac{1}{4})^{-2}$; $(\frac{1}{27})^{\frac{1}{3}}$; $(\frac{1}{27})^{-\frac{1}{3}}$; $(68)^0$.

22. What is the value of $10^{\log_{10} 4}$?

23. From a table of logarithms, find: $\log_{10} 73.4$; $\log_{10} 734$; $\log_{10} 0.00896$; $\log_{10} 8.96$. Find the numbers whose logarithms (to the base 10) are: 2.7048; -0.4903; 1.7577.

24. Evaluate: $\log_3 27^{\frac{2}{3}}$; $\log_5 \sqrt{125}$; $\log_4 (\frac{1}{4})^{\frac{3}{8}}$; $\log_{10} 10^{-\frac{2}{3}}$.

25. Find the following logarithms: $\log_2 64$; $\log_3 27$; $\log_{10} 10$; $\log_{100} 10$; $\log_{100} 100$; $\log_e (1/e^2)$; $\log_3 \sqrt[3]{27^2}$; $\log_{37} 1$.

26. Using a table of logarithms to the base 10, solve the equation $5^x = 300$. What does your solution tell you about the logarithm of 300 to the base 5? Find the logarithm of 300 to the base 5 by using Eq. 2-24.

27. Solve for v in terms of u: $\log_a v = u$; $\log_{10} v = -5u$; $\log_3 v = 3 \log_3 u$.

28. Under what conditions is $\log_a (p + q) = \log_a p + \log_a q$?

29. Identify the geometric and arithmetic progressions among the following: 1, 7, 13, 19, 27, 35, . . . ; 1, 3, 9, 27, . . . ; 1, $\frac{1}{2}$, $\frac{1}{3}$, $\frac{1}{4}$, $\frac{1}{5}$, $\frac{1}{6}$, . . . ; 7.5, 9.0, 10.5, 12.0, . . . ; 1.5, 2.5, 3.5, 4.5, 5.5, . . . ; $\frac{1}{2}$, $\frac{1}{4}$, $\frac{1}{8}$, $\frac{1}{16}$, $\frac{1}{32}$, . . . ; $\frac{1}{2}$, $\frac{1}{8}$, $\frac{1}{32}$, . . . ; $\frac{1}{2}$, $\frac{1}{8}$, $\frac{1}{16}$, $\frac{1}{32}$, . . .

30. Find the sum of the following two infinite series: $1 + \frac{1}{2} + \frac{1}{4} + \frac{1}{8} + \frac{1}{16} + \cdots$; $1 - \frac{1}{2} + \frac{1}{4} - \frac{1}{8} + \frac{1}{16} - \cdots$

31. Find the sum of the odd numbers between 0 and 100.

32. A ball is dropped from a height of 27 meters. Subsequent to each rebound it rises to two-thirds the height from which it fell. How high does it rise on the seventh rebound? How far has it traveled by the time it reaches the top of the tenth rebound? by the time it comes to rest?

33. The first term of an arithmetic progression is 2, and the thirteenth term is 38. What is the difference between consecutive terms?

34. Find the sum of the following infinite series:

$$\frac{1}{5} + \frac{2}{5^2} + \frac{1}{5^3} + \frac{2}{5^4} + \frac{1}{5^5} + \frac{2}{5^6} + \cdots$$

35. "The sum of the first ten terms of an arithmetic progression is four times the sum of the first five terms." Is this enough information to find the difference (d) between consecutive terms? If so, what is d? If not, what *does* the statement provide?

36. Find the value of $3 - 2x + x^2$ when $x = 2 - 3i$.
37. Simplify the following as much as possible: $3i^7$; i^{18}; $-5i^{76}$; i^{17}.
38. Show that $(1 + i)/\sqrt{2}$ is the square root of i (i.e., $= \sqrt{i}$). Can you find $\sqrt{-i}$?
39. Given that y is proportional to x^3, and that $y = 4$ when $x = 2$, what is y when $x = 3$? What is the proportionality constant linking y and x^3?
40. We are told that the rate of flow of gasoline into an automobile tank is proportional to the cross section of the pump hose. If it takes 3.5 min to fill a tank with a hose 1 in. in diameter, how long will it take to fill the same tank with a hose $1\frac{1}{4}$ in. in diameter?

3

GRAPHS AND
ANALYTIC
GEOMETRY[1]

1. WHAT A GRAPH IS

The purpose of a graph is to display quantities visually, i.e.,
to put statements involving numerical magnitudes into pictorial
form. The basic idea of a graph is the one-to-one correspondence
that can be established between numbers and the points on a line.
Any straight line can have all the numbers, in their proper order,
marked off along it, and this can be done in a number of ways
(see Fig. 3-1).[2] We shall be concerned for the most part with the
correspondence shown in (c), where equal numerical intervals are
assigned equal lengths, so that the length of a segment is directly

[1] For further details, see any standard text in analytic geometry, such
as *Analytic Geometry* by R. E. Johnson and N. H. McCoy (New York: Holt,
Rinehart & Winston, 1955).

[2] This is true about open *curved* lines as well, but we shall restrict ourselves for the purposes of the present discussion to straight lines.

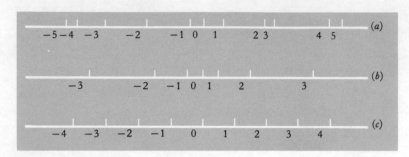

Fig. 3-1

proportional to its corresponding numerical magnitude. The first step in plotting a graph is to decide how great a numerical magnitude will be taken to correspond to a line segment of given length (e.g., how many units—1, 2, 5, or 10, or some other number—will correspond to 1 cm). Once this is done, the line can be drawn, and the numbers marked off. The line is called a *coordinate axis*. If physical quantities are involved, the units and correspondence chosen must, of course, be clearly indicated (e.g., "1 cm = 10 cents").

2. KINDS OF GRAPHS. DIMENSIONALITY

A graph where only *one* quantity is plotted is called a one-dimensional graph, since only one line is used (and hence only one dimension of space comes into play). Examples of such graphs, shown in Fig. 3-2, are indicators of the cost of living index, plots of the amount of money raised in a community chest drive, and certain kinds of automobile speedometers which display the speed as proportional to the length of a horizontal red bar.

A graph where *two* functionally related quantities are plotted is called a two-dimensional graph. Usually, the two coordinate axes used to represent the two quantities are drawn perpendicular

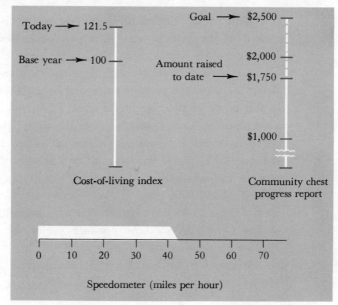

Today ——▶ 121.5 ——

Base year ——▶ 100 ——

Cost-of-living index

Goal ——▶ $2,500 ——

Amount raised
to date ——▶

$2,000 ——

$1,750 ——

$1,000 ——

Community chest
progress report

| 0 | 10 | 20 | 30 | 40 | 50 | 60 | 70 |

Fig. 3-2

Speedometer (miles per hour)

to each other; such a coordinate system is called a Cartesian coordinate system, after René Descartes, whose book on analytic geometry (published in 1637) was one of the earliest classics on the subject.

The functional relationship between the variables associates with each value of one variable a value of the other variable.[3] By convention, this is displayed graphically by associating with the pair of related values *a single point* in the plane of the two axes. The point is located directly above the value for the variable plotted horizontally and directly across from the related value for the variable plotted vertically. Figure 3-3 illustrates how the point corresponding to the (x, y) pair $(1, 25)$, related by the equation $y = 25x$, is assigned for the case where the x coordinate axis

[3] This does not exclude the possibility that with a given value of one variable there are associated two or more values of the other—e.g., in the function $y = x^2$, to each value of y correspond two values of x (a positive and a negative value). The procedure outlined in the text is in this case applied to each of the two pairs of values.

is chosen as the horizontal axis, and the *y* coordinate axis is chosen as the vertical axis. The pair of values are called the *coordinates of the point* and may be written next to the point.

A functional relationship between two variables yields a whole set of related number pairs, and hence a whole set of points in the plane of the coordinate axes. These points may describe a continuous curve (possibly more than one) in the plane; this curve is called *the graph of the function*. The graph of $y = 25x$ is shown in Fig. 3-4. Examples of two-dimensional graphs are a plot of the relationship between cost-of-living index and time (which shows how the cost of living varies with time) or a plot of the relationship between pressure and volume for a sample of gas (which shows how pressure varies with volume). (See Fig. 3-5.)

When *three* functionally related quantities are plotted, the

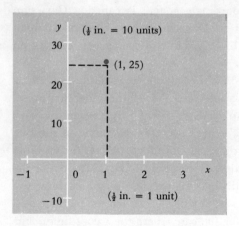

Fig. 3-3   Location of the point (1, 25) in a Cartesian (x, y) coordinate system. Note that the scale used for the x-axis may be chosen to be different from that used for the y-axis, as is the case in this figure.

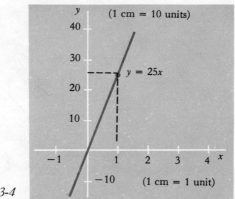

Fig. 3-4

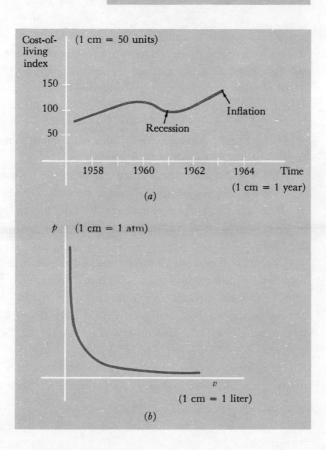

Fig. 3-5

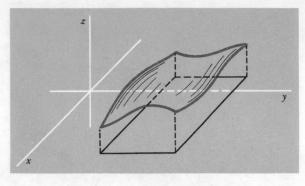

Fig. 3-6

graph is three-dimensional. Usually a Cartesian coordinate system is used, where the three coordinate axes are drawn perpendicular to each other. In this case, each point in space corresponds to a *triplet* of related values (x, y, z), and the correspondence is set up exactly in the same way as in the two-dimensional case. The functional relationship yields a set of number triplets and hence a set of points. These points may describe a continuous surface in space (again called the graph of the function).

A three-dimensional plot should properly be made in three dimensions, but perspective allows us to make a two-dimensional drawing of a three-dimensional graph. This makes it possible for us to exhibit three-dimensional graphs on the printed page (see Fig. 3-6).

To make the graph of a function relating four or more variables, we would require four or more dimensions. Since more than three dimensions are not available to us, such graphs are never drawn but are only talked about (in language that draws heavily on the analogies with two- or three-dimensional graphs).

It is important to remember always to specify what is being plotted—i.e., what the various coordinate axes represent and what units are being used. When graphs of functions are being discussed in general terms, without reference to particular kinds of quantities, the coordinate axes are usually labeled with pure numbers (i.e., labeled "1, 2, 3, . . ." or "10, 20, 30, . . ." without specifying whether we are plotting cost in dollars, volume in liters, or some other physical quantity).

3. ANALYTIC GEOMETRY

By the procedure just outlined, a picture or geometrical figure can always be associated with any given function (viz., "the graph of the function"). Conversely, given an arbitrary geometrical figure or graph, a function can always be found, the graph of which is the given figure. (If necessary, this can be done by *defining* the function through the set of related number pairs that are the coordinates of the points composing the given graph.) The study of the graphical correlation between geometrical figures and algebraic functions is generally called *analytic geometry*. Analytic geometry is concerned solely with the relationship between functions and graphs; it does not take into consideration the *nature* of the quantities being plotted (i.e., their dimensions or physical properties).

Since geometric forms are endlessly varied, and their interesting features are inexhaustible, the study of analytic geometry also offers unlimited variety. We shall discuss here only those few figures that come up over and over again in the study of science. These are the straight line, the circle, the right hyperbola, the increasing and decreasing exponentials, and the logarithmic curve. In addition, there are two trigonometric curves that recur frequently that we shall discuss in Chapter 4. (Chapter 4 should also be consulted for definitions of the trigonometric terms used here.)

4. THE STRAIGHT LINE

A straight line is a curve that never changes its direction. Suppose we have a straight line lying in a plane, in which we have chosen two Cartesian coordinate axes, one labeled x, the other labeled y. (If a third variable is introduced, it is customarily labeled z.) In terms of these, we can restate our definition as follows: a straight line (in a plane) is a planar curve that always makes the same angle with the direction of the x-axis. This means that at *any* point on a straight line, the angle between the line and the x-direction is the same (Fig. 3-7). The functional relationship between x and y corresponding to a straight line can be found by translating the definition into the language of algebra, as follows: Consider an arbitrary straight line passing through some point [the coordinates of which are (α, β)] and making an angle θ with the x-direction (see Fig. 3-8). According to the definition of a straight line, another point [with arbitrary coordinates (x, y)] will lie on this straight line if and only if the segment connecting (α, β) and (x, y) makes an angle θ with the x-direction (see Fig. 3-9). Thus, in order for the point (x, y) to lie on the line, we must have (as Fig. 3-9 shows):

$$(y - \beta)/(x - \alpha) = \tan \theta \tag{3-1}$$
$$y - \beta = (x - \alpha) \tan \theta = x \tan \theta - \alpha \tan \theta$$
$$y = x \tan \theta + (\beta - \alpha \tan \theta) \tag{3-2}$$

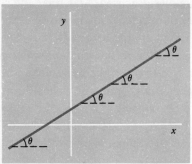

Fig. 3-7

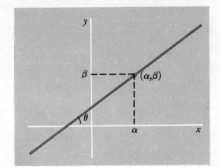

Fig. 3-8

where, α, β, and θ have all been defined above. In other words, the coordinates (x, y) of any point lying on the line must be related by a linear relation of the form

$$y = mx + b \qquad\qquad (3\text{-}3)$$

where m and b are constants; specifically, where

$$m \equiv \tan\theta \qquad\qquad (3\text{-}4)$$

and b is a constant. The quantity $m \equiv \tan\theta$ is called *the slope of the line*. To see the significance of b, we note that when $x = 0$ (i.e., when we are on the y-axis), then $y = b$. One of the points on the line is, then, the point $(0, b)$. This point is called the

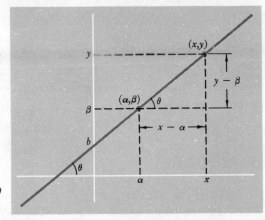

Fig. 3-9

y-intercept of the curve, since it is the point where the curve inter-
cepts the *y*-axis.

Conversely, suppose we have an arbitrary linear relationship
between two variables, such as

$$Ay + Bx + C = 0 \tag{3-5}$$

If $A \neq 0$, this can always be brought to the form of Eq. 3-3 by
solving for *y*. The resulting equation is $y = -(B/A)x - (C/A)$,
and represents a straight line of slope $-(B/A)$ and *y*-intercept
$-(C/A)$. If $A = 0$, we are dealing with the case $Bx + C = 0$ or
$x = -(C/B) \equiv a$, where *a* is some constant. The relation $x = a$
involves only one variable; when plotted in two dimensions (on a
plane) its graph (Fig. 3-10) is a straight line perpendicular to the

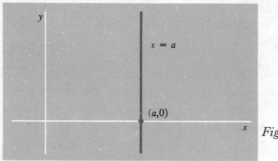

Fig. 3-10

x-axis at $x = a$, indicating that regardless of the value assigned to
y (which does not, in fact, even enter the picture) the value of *x* is
always *a*. Thus, any linear relationship like Eq. 3-5 has as its
graph a straight line.

5. THE CIRCLE

A circle is a planar curve all of whose points are equidistant
from a given point, called the *center*. The distance from the curve
to the center is called the *radius* of the circle. An algebraic relation

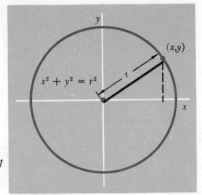

Fig. 3-11

whose graph is a circle is found as follows. Consider a circle of radius r, with the center at the intersection of the coordinate axes (at "the origin of the coordinate system"). (See Fig. 3-11.) Then, if a point with coordinates (x, y) lies on the circle, the coordinates must obey the relation

$$x^2 + y^2 = r^2 \qquad\qquad (3\text{-}6)$$

which is simply Pythagoras' theorem applied to the right triangle (x, y, r). Conversely, any point with coordinates that obey Eq. 3-6 is a distance r from the origin and hence lies on the circle.

6. THE RIGHT HYPERBOLA

The functional relation

$$y = a/x \qquad \text{or} \qquad xy = a \qquad\qquad (3\text{-}7)$$

when plotted yields a curve known as a right hyperbola (Fig. 3-12). This curve has two separate branches, one for positive values of x and y, the other for negative values of x and y. From Eq. 3-7 we see that as $|x|$ becomes smaller, $|y|$ becomes larger (as $x \to 0$, $y \to \infty$ for the upper branch; as $x \to 0$, $y \to -\infty$ for the lower branch); and as $y \to 0$, $x \to \pm \infty$ (the upper sign for the upper branch, the lower sign for the lower branch). The curve never

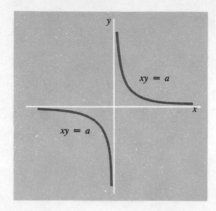

Fig. 3-12

intersects the *x* or *y* axes, although it approaches closer and closer to them as one proceeds to its extremities. The *x* and *y* axes are called the *asymptotes* of the hyperbola, and the curve is said to approach the *x* and *y* axes *asymptotically*.

7. INCREASING AND DECREASING EXPONENTIALS

The graphs of the functions $y = a^x$ (increasing exponential) and $y = a^{-x}$ ($\equiv 1/a^x$) (decreasing exponential) are shown in

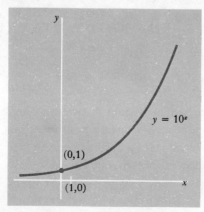

Fig. 3-13

Figs. 3-13 and 3-14 for the special case $a = 10$. The choice of base is arbitrary, and the curves have the same form for any base. [Both pass through the point $(0, 1)$, regardless of base.] The increasing exponential rises steeply. For the base $a = 10$, points having, for example, x-coordinates 2, 3, and 4 have y-coordinates 100, 1,000, and 10,000, respectively. The decreasing exponential drops steeply. For the base $a = 10$, points having, for example,

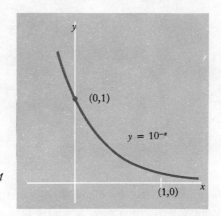

Fig. 3-14

x-coordinates 2, 3, and 4 have y-coordinates 0.01, 0.001, and 0.0001, respectively. This curve approaches the x-axis asymptotically (as $x \to \infty$, $y \to 0$), as can be seen directly from the relation $y = a^{-x}$. Note that the part of (a) corresponding to negative x is just (b) for positive x (flipped over—i.e., reflected through the y-axis) and (b) for negative x is just (a) for positive x [reflected through the y-axis].

8. THE LOGARITHMIC CURVE

The graph of the function $y = \log_a x$ is shown in Fig. 3-15 for the special case $a = 10$. Again, as was true for exponentials, the form of the curve is the same for any base. The curve approaches the negative y-axis asymptotically (as $x \to 0$, $y \to -\infty$), as we know from the properties of the logarithm function (listed in Chapter 2, Section 5). The x-intercept is always at $x = 1$, regardless of base. The curve rises slowly. For the base $a = 10$,

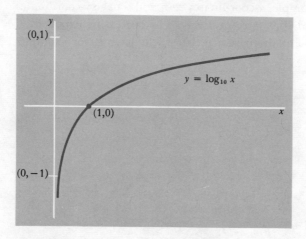

Fig. 3-15

points having, for example, x-coordinates 100, 1,000, and 10,000, have y-coordinates 2, 3, and 4 respectively. But, although it rises slowly, the curve goes on rising as x gets larger.

9. TRANSFORMATIONS OF COORDINATES

There are occasions when we wish to change from one set of coordinate axes to a different set of axes. Such a change is called a *transformation of coordinates*. There exist three basic types of transformation, with the aid of which any arbitrary transformation can be carried out (by successive application of one, two, or all three of the basic transformations): *translation*, *rotation*, and *reflection*. We shall restrict ourselves initially to transformations in two dimensions. The original coordinate system will be referred to with unprimed letters and the new coordinate system, with primed letters.

A *translation* is a transformation in which the new coordinate axes are parallel to the old ones, while the new origin O' is displaced from the old origin O, as shown in Fig. 3-16. Let the new origin O' be located at a point whose coordinates are (h, k) in the

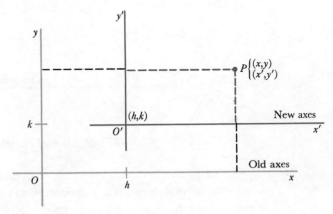

Fig. 3-16   Translation of coordinates.

old system, as shown. Consider an arbitrary point P, having coordinates (x, y) in the old system, and (x', y') in the new system. From the figure it can be seen that the old and new coordinates of P are related by the following *transformation equations:*

$$\left. \begin{aligned} x' &= x - h \\ y' &= y - k \end{aligned} \right\} \begin{aligned} &\text{Translation, in which the origin} \\ &\text{goes from } (O, O) \text{ to } (h, k) \end{aligned} \qquad (3\text{-}8)$$

A *rotation* (through an angle θ) is a transformation in which the origins O and O' coincide, while the new axes are inclined by a positive (counterclockwise) rotation of angle θ relative to the old axes. In the case of a rotation, the old and new coordinates of an arbitrary point P are related by the following transformation equations (see Fig. 3-17).

$$\left. \begin{aligned} x' &= x \cos \theta + y \sin \theta \\ y' &= -x \sin \theta + y \cos \theta \end{aligned} \right\} \begin{aligned} &\text{Rotation, through} \\ &\text{an angle } \theta \end{aligned} \qquad (3\text{-}9)$$

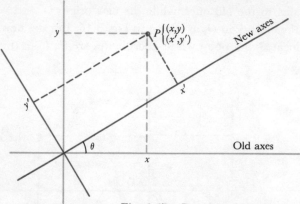

Fig. 3-17   Rotation of coordinates.

A *reflection in the x-axis* is a transformation in which the origins O and O' and the x-axes x and x' coincide, while the y' axis is directed in a sense opposite to the y-axis. A *reflection in the y-axis* is a transformation in which the origins O and O' and the y-axes y and y' coincide, while the x' axis is directed in a sense opposite to the x-axis. The nomenclature is suggested by the fact, apparent from Figs. 3-18, 3-19, and 3-20, that the new axes can be obtained from the old by *reflecting* the old axes in a mirror placed on the axis in which the reflection is made. The transformation equations

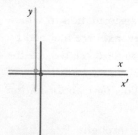

Fig. 3-18   Reflection in the x-axis.

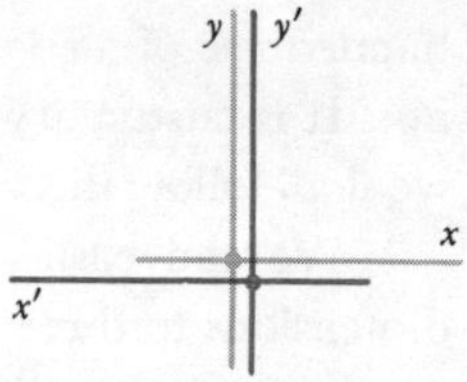

*Fig. 3-19   Reflection in
the y-axis.*

are:

$$x' = x \Big\} \begin{array}{l}\text{Reflection in}\\ \text{the } x\text{-axis}\end{array} \quad x' = -x \Big\} \begin{array}{l}\text{Reflection in}\\ \text{the } y\text{-axis}\end{array} \quad (3\text{-}10)$$
$$y' = -y$$

A *reflection in the origin* is a transformation in which *both axes* are reversed in sense, as if the coordinate system were reflected in the origin. This transformation is equivalent to successive reflections in the *x* and *y* axes. It should also be noted that, in two dimensions, a reflection in the origin is equivalent to a rotation of coordinates through an angle of 180°. The transformation equations are:

$$x' = -x \Big\} \begin{array}{l}\text{Reflection in}\\ \text{the origin}\end{array} \quad (3\text{-}11)$$
$$y' = -y$$

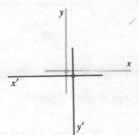

*Fig. 3-20   Reflection in
the origin.*

By convention, a two-dimensional coordinate system is called a *right-handed coordinate system* if the *y*-axis is reached by rotating the *x*-axis through a positive (counterclockwise) angle of 90°. If the *y*-axis is reached by rotating the *x*-axis through a negative (clockwise) angle of 90°, the coordinate system is called a *left-handed coordinate system.* Note that a reflection in an axis changes the handedness of a coordinate system; a reflection in the origin does not. It is customary to use right-handed coordinate systems, and we shall follow this convention, except where otherwise stipulated.

We can easily extend the definitions given above for two dimensions to three dimensions. In the case of reflections, we also speak of *reflections in coordinate planes*, as illustrated in Fig. 3-21.

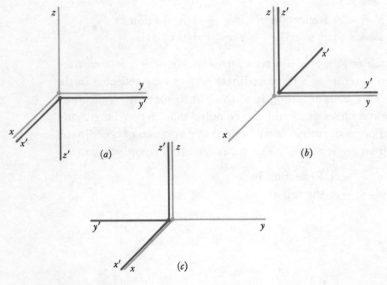

Fig. 3-21 (*a*) *Reflection in the x-y plane.* (*b*) *Reflection in the y-z plane.*
(*c*) *Reflection in the x-z plane.*

A right-handed coordinate system in three dimensions is defined analogously to one in two dimensions (the *y*-axis is reached by rotating the *x*-axis through a positive 90° angle in the *x-y* plane; the *z*-axis is reached by rotating the *y*-axis through a positive 90° angle in the *y-z* plane). The definition can be simplified by reference to the *right hand:* a coordinate system is right-handed if the *x*, *y*, *z* axes (in that order) correspond to the thumb, index finger, and middle finger of the right hand (in that order) when these three fingers are extended perpendicular to each other (Fig. 3-22). A left-handed coordinate system can be defined in the same way, by reference to the left hand. In three dimensions, a

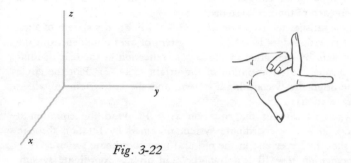

Fig. 3-22

reflection in a coordinate plane, or in the origin, changes the handedness of a system.

As in two dimensions, it is customary to use right-handed coordinate systems in three dimensions. We shall follow this custom, except where otherwise stipulated.

EXERCISES

1. Plot the graphs of the functions determined in Exercises 11 and 12 to Chapter 2.
2. The points $(1, -1)$, $(3, 3)$, and $(7, k)$ lie on the same line. What is k?
3. When a linear equation is written in the form of Eq. 3-3, it is said to be in the *slope-intercept form* (for reasons that should be obvious from the text). Write in the slope-intercept form the equations for the straight lines specified as follows: slope = 3, y-intercept = 5; slope = $\frac{1}{2}$, y-intercept = 2; slope = 2, passes through the point $(3, 7)$; slope = 1, passes through $(-1, -3)$; passes through $(0, 2)$ and $(1, 0)$; passes through $(-5, -4)$ and $(-3, -2)$; passes through $(2, 5)$ and $(3, 1)$.

4. What kind of figure is formed when the points of intersection of the curves $xy = 12$ and $x^2 + y^2 = 25$ are joined by straight-line segments?

5. A line satisfies the equation $y = 2x$, in an x, y coordinate system. Find the equations for that line in new coordinate systems related to the x, y system through the following transformations: reflection in the y-axis; translation of the origin to $(1, 3)$; rotation of the axes through $60°$. Plot the graphs of the line in the original x, y system and in each of the new systems.

6. A circle satisfies the equation $x^2 + y^2 = 36$ in an x, y system of axes. What equation does it satisfy in a system of axes obtained from the x, y system by: reflection in the x-axis; reflection in the origin; rotation through $45°$; translation of the origin to $(4, 3)$? Plot the circle in the original x, y coordinate system, and the last system (obtained by translation).

7. A hyperbola satisfies the equation $xy = 16$. Find the equation it satisfies in a new coordinate system obtained by rotation through $45°$. Plot the hyperbola in the old and new coordinate system.

8. The equation $st = 10$ is a hyperbola in an s, t coordinate system, that is, when s is plotted against t. Could we plot s as a function of something other than t, so that the resulting graph would be a straight line? Can we do the same with $s = \log_{10} t$? Can we do the same in every instance? If the answer is "yes" to one or more of these questions, is there any point to knowing this?

4

TRIGONOMETRY[1]

1. ANGLE

An angle can be defined qualitatively as the spread between two lines that meet at a point or as the degree of inclination of one line to another which it intersects. We often speak of an angle as being *generated* by the rotation of one line (the *generator*) away from another (the *base*) with their intersection (the *vertex*) as the pivot (Fig. 4-1). An angle is *positive* if the generator rotates in the counterclockwise direction. For any negative angle a positive

[1] For an elementary introduction to trigonometry see any standard text, such as J. B. Rosenbach, E. A. Whitman, and D. Moskovitz, *Essentials of Trigonometry* (2nd ed., New York: Blaisdell, 1961). For a more concise and more advanced treatment containing applications of special value to science, see R. R. Christian, *A Brief Trigonometry* (preliminary ed., New York: Blaisdell, 1962).

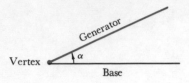

Fig. 4-1

angle can be found having the same trigonometric properties
(see Fig. 4-2), so that we need only consider positive angles.

In order to obtain a quantitative definition of an angle, we
need to devise some way to *measure* an angle. The smallest angle
that can exist is one in which there is *no* spread between the
generator and the base; this angle is zero no matter what units
are used for angle measure. The angle gets larger as the spread
between base and generator gets larger, until the generator has
completed a full revolution and meets the base again (Fig. 4-3).
As the generator rotates further, it generates new angles that are
identical to smaller angles (Fig. 4-4). Thus the basic range for

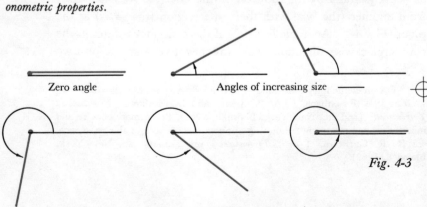

Fig. 4-2   (a) *Negative angle.* (b) *Positive angle with the same trigonometric properties.*

Fig. 4-3

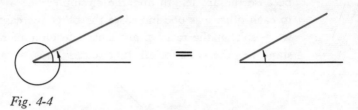

Fig. 4-4

angle measure lies between zero rotation of the generator and one complete rotation of the generator; all negative angles and all angles generated by more than one complete rotation are identical in all their properties to angles that lie in the basic range.

One standard way to measure angles is to divide the full revolution into 360 equal parts, calling each part a *degree* (°). Thus, in this system of measure, a full revolution generates an angle of 360°, a half revolution generates an angle of 180°, a quarter revolution generates an angle of 90°, and so forth. Each degree is further subdivided into 60 equal parts, called *minutes* ('), and these in turn are each divided into 60 equal parts called *seconds* ("). This system of measure is very widely used, despite the fact that it is entirely arbitrary, and there is nothing at all "natural" about it. We shall almost never use this system of measure.

A second way to measure angles is suggested by the properties of an angle and is widely used by mathematicians and scientists. As the generator rotates to its final position, any point on it sweeps out a circular arc segment. The size of the angle that has been generated can be measured by considering *the fraction of the total circumference intercepted by the sides of the angle.* In other words, we can take the size of the angle to be proportional to *the ratio of the arc length intercepted by the angle to the total circumference* (of the circle of which the arc length is a segment). Note that it is not important which arc is chosen. Any arc, swept out by any point on the generator, will do, since the ratio s/c

is the same for all arcs (e.g., $s/c = s'/c'$ in Fig. 4-5). (This is because the arc length and the circumference are proportional to each other—as one increases the other increases in the same way—so that the ratio of arc length to circumference is a constant, i.e., the same for all the circles.) Thus, a natural measure

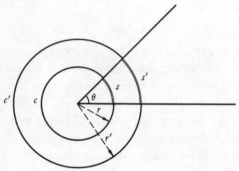

Fig. 4-5

for an angle θ would be something proportional to the ratio s/c:

$$\theta \propto s/c = s/2\pi r = \left(\frac{1}{2\pi}\right)(s/r) \tag{4-1}$$

It turns out that the factor $\left(\frac{1}{2\pi}\right)$ is an inconvenience, especially when problems involving calculus are encountered (as we shall see). The constant of proportionality is therefore chosen to be 2π (i.e., $\theta \equiv (2\pi)s/c = s/r$) in order to make this factor disappear. The exact measure of an angle, in this system, is thus taken to be the pure ratio of lengths s/r, and the unit of measure is called a *radian* (rad):

$$\theta \equiv s/r \quad \text{(in radians)} \tag{4-2}$$

In words, *the number of radians in an angle is the ratio of the arc length s intercepted by the angle to the radius of the circle of which s is a segment.* It should be noted that θ thus defined is a ratio formed from two quantities having the same physical dimensions, length, so that θ itself is physically dimensionless (i.e., is a pure number).

One gets used to radian measure in the same way one gets used to degree measure—through practice and use. To convert from degrees to radians simply recall that one complete revolution of the generator gives an angle of 360° in degree measure, and an angle $s/r = 2\pi r/r = 2\pi$ rad in radian measure, since the arc length intercepted by a full revolution is the entire circumference, $s = 2\pi r$. Thus

$$
\begin{aligned}
2\pi \text{ rad} &= 360° \\
1 \text{ rad} &= (360/2\pi)° = (180/\pi)° \\
\theta \text{ rad} &= (180 \cdot \theta/\pi)° \\
(\pi/180) \text{ rad} &= 1° \qquad\qquad\qquad\qquad (4\text{-}3)
\end{aligned}
$$

The following table gives the conversion figures for some commonly encountered angles:

Angle (°)	0	30	45	60	90	120	180	270	360
Angle (rad)	0	$\pi/6$	$\pi/4$	$\pi/3$	$\pi/2$	$2\pi/3$	π	$3\pi/2$	2π

(4-4)

Note that the basic range of angle measure in radians is from 0 to 2π.

2. TRIGONOMETRIC FUNCTIONS OF ACUTE ANGLES[2]

Given an acute angle α, form a right triangle by dropping a perpendicular to the base from any point on the generator. The two basic trigonometric functions of α are defined as follows:

1. The sine (sin) function:

$$\sin \alpha \equiv y/r \qquad (y = r \sin \alpha) \qquad\qquad (4\text{-}5)$$

[2] An acute angle is an angle smaller than $\pi/2$ rad ($= 90°$).

2. The cosine (cos) function:

$$\cos \alpha \equiv x/r \qquad (x = r \cos \alpha) \qquad (4\text{-}6)$$

These functions are independent of the particular point chosen on the generator from which the perpendicular is dropped. From Fig. 4-6 it can be seen that $x/r = x'/r'$, $y/r = y'/r'$, since the two

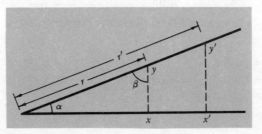

Fig. 4-6

triangles shown—as well as any other right triangle so formed— are similar triangles.

The angle β shown in the figure is called the *complementary angle* to α—i.e., two angles are complementary if their sum is a right angle. Applying the Definitions 4-5 and 4-6 to β, we see that the trigonometric functions of complementary angles are related as follows:

$$\left.\begin{array}{l} \sin \beta = \cos \alpha \\ \cos \beta = \sin \alpha \end{array}\right\} \text{ where } \beta = \pi/2 - \alpha \qquad (4\text{-}7)$$

The two basic trigonometric functions are related by a fundamental trigonometric identity that follows directly from Pythagoras' theorem, $x^2 + y^2 = r^2$; namely,

$$\sin^2 \alpha + \cos^2 \alpha = 1 \qquad (4\text{-}8)$$

There is a third trigonometric function derived from these two that often finds use:

3. The tangent (tan) function:

$$\tan \alpha \equiv y/x = \sin \alpha/\cos \alpha \qquad (4\text{-}9)$$

3. TRIGONOMETRIC FUNCTIONS OF ARBITRARY ANGLES

The Definitions 4-5 and 4-6 can be extended to arbitrary angles as follows. Given an arbitrary angle, draw a set of Cartesian axes in the plane of the angle, having the origin at the vertex of the angle and the *x*-axis along the base of the angle. The coordinate axes divide the plane into four *quadrants*, labeled I to IV, starting with the upper right quadrant and proceeding counterclockwise. If the generator lies in the first quadrant, the angle is an acute angle, and the functions are defined as in Definitions 4-5 and 4-6 with *x* and *y* the coordinates of an arbitrary point on the generator and *r* the distance from the origin

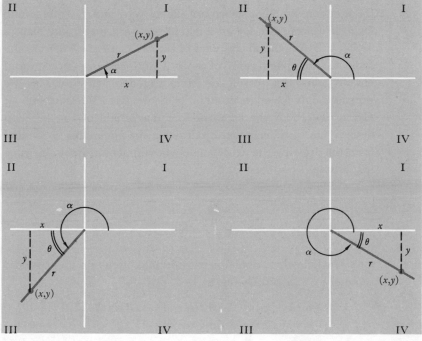

Fig. 4-7

to the point. If the generator lies in quadrants II, III, or IV, the angle is no longer acute, but *the functions are still defined by Definitions 4.5 and 4.6*, with x and y the coordinates of a point on the generator and r the distance from the origin to the point.

From Fig. 4-7 it can be seen that for an angle in quadrants II or III, x—and hence the cosine—is negative; for an angle in quadrants I or IV, x—and the cosine—is positive; for an angle in quadrants III or IV, y—and hence the sine—is negative; for an angle in quadrants I and II, y—and the sine—is positive. Thus we can determine by inspection the correct *sign* of the trigonometric function in question.

As for the *magnitude* of the trigonometric functions of angles in quadrants II, III, or IV, we can see from the figure that the magnitudes of the functions of α are equal to the magnitudes of the functions of the *acute angle* θ (being $|x/r|$ and $|y/r|$ for α and for θ). For example, for an angle in the third quadrant, such as $4\pi/3$ ($= 240°$), the magnitudes of $\sin 4\pi/3$ and $\cos 4\pi/3$ are the same as the magnitudes of $\sin \pi/3$ and $\cos \pi/3$ ($\sin 60°$ and $\cos 60°$). For this reason, tables of trigonometric functions are prepared only for acute angles. For angles lying in quadrants II, III, or IV, both the sign and the magnitude of the function desired can be determined by drawing the angle and by finding from the drawing the acute angle whose functions have the same magnitude.

4. SOME TRIGONOMETRIC FORMULAS

The following trigonometric formulas often find use. (θ and ϕ represent two arbitrary angles.)

$$\sin (\theta \pm \phi) = \sin \theta \cos \phi \pm \cos \theta \sin \phi \qquad (4\text{-}10)$$
$$\sin 2\theta = 2 \sin \theta \cos \theta \qquad (4\text{-}11)$$
$$\cos (\theta \pm \phi) = \cos \theta \cos \phi \mp \sin \theta \sin \phi \qquad (4\text{-}12)$$

$$\cos 2\theta = \cos^2 \theta - \sin^2 \theta \qquad (4\text{-}13)$$

$$\sin \theta/2 = \sqrt{(1/2)(1 - \cos \theta)} \qquad (4\text{-}14)$$

$$\cos \theta/2 = \sqrt{(1/2)(1 + \cos \theta)} \qquad (4\text{-}15)$$

$$\cos \theta + \cos \phi = 2 \cos \left(\frac{\theta + \phi}{2}\right) \cos \left(\frac{\theta - \phi}{2}\right) \qquad (4\text{-}16)$$

$$\cos \theta - \cos \phi = -2 \sin \left(\frac{\theta + \phi}{2}\right) \sin \left(\frac{\theta - \phi}{2}\right) \qquad (4\text{-}17)$$

$$\sin \theta \sin \phi = \tfrac{1}{2} \cos (\theta - \phi) - \tfrac{1}{2} \cos (\theta + \phi) \qquad (4\text{-}18)$$

$$\cos \theta \cos \phi = \tfrac{1}{2} \cos (\theta - \phi) + \tfrac{1}{2} \cos (\theta + \phi) \qquad (4\text{-}19)$$

$$\sin \theta \cos \phi = \tfrac{1}{2} \sin (\theta - \phi) + \tfrac{1}{2} \sin (\theta + \phi) \qquad (4\text{-}20)$$

5. FUNCTIONS OF SPECIAL ANGLES

Certain angles have trigonometric functions whose values are easy to calculate. It is worth knowing how to calculate these values, since the angles in question come up frequently.

1. 0 rad (0°): The generator and the base coincide, so that $x = r, y = 0$. Hence, $\sin 0 = 0$, $\cos 0 = 1$.

2. $\pi/2$ rad (90°): The generator lies on the y-axis, so that $x = 0, y = r$. Hence, $\sin \pi/2 = 1$, $\cos \pi/2 = 0$.

3. The results obtained in 1 and 2 can be extended to π rad, $3\pi/2$ rad, and 2π rad by drawing the angles. The results are: $\sin \pi = 0$, $\cos \pi = -1$; $\sin 3\pi/2 = -1$, $\cos 3\pi/2 = 0$; $\sin 2\pi = \sin 0 = 0$, $\cos 2\pi = \cos 0 = 1$.

4. $\pi/6$ rad (30°) and $\pi/3$ rad (60°)—two complementary angles: The functions of these angles can be found by bisecting an equilateral triangle and applying Pythagoras' theorem to find the height. Doing this, we find that $\sin \pi/3 = \sqrt{3}/2 = .866$, $\cos \pi/3 = \tfrac{1}{2} = .500$; $\sin \pi/6 = \tfrac{1}{2} = .500$, $\cos \pi/6 = \sqrt{3}/2 = .866$ (Fig. 4-8). These results can be extended to angles in quadrants II, III, or IV that are multiples of $\pi/6$.

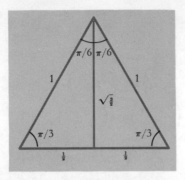

Fig. 4-8

5. $\pi/4$ rad (45°): In this case the complementary angle is also $\pi/4$ rad (hence, sin $\pi/4$ = cos $\pi/4$), so we are dealing with an isosceles right triangle. From Fig. 4-9, with the aid of

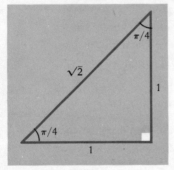

Fig. 4-9

Pythagoras' theorem, we find sin $\pi/4$ = cos $\pi/4$ = $1/\sqrt{2}$ = .707.

6. GRAPHS OF THE TRIGONOMETRIC FUNCTIONS

Using the values found above, and other values for other angles given in the tables, we can draw graphs of the two basic functions $y = \sin x$ and $y = \cos x$. These graphs are shown in Fig. 4-10. Note that both graphs simply repeat the section between 0 and 2π in the intervals 2π to 4π, 4π to 6π, 6π to 8π, etc. and

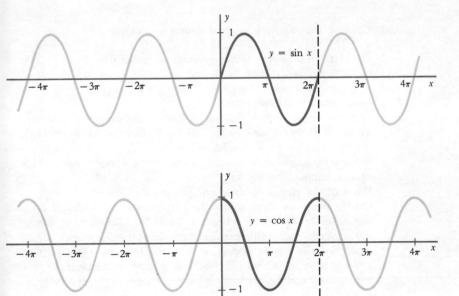

Fig. 4-10

−2π to 0, −4π to −2π, −6π to −4π, etc. This corresponds to the fact, discussed earlier, that the basic range of variation for angles is the range 0 to 2π, and that in other succeeding or preceding intervals of width 2π, all the properties of the basic interval are repeated. Functions that repeat themselves in succeeding intervals of the range of the variable are called *periodic functions*, and the magnitude of the basic interval is called *the period of the function*. In the case of the sine and cosine functions, the period is 2π.

EXERCISES

1. Find the positive angle lying within the basic range (0 − 2π) whose properties are the same as the following angles: −π/4; −π; 3π; 6.8π; −2π; −1; −4.8; 2.5π.

2. Convert the following angle-measures in degrees to radians: 10°; 57°; 135°; 210°; 240°; 270°; 300°; 350°.

3. Convert the following angle-measures in radians to degrees: 1; 3; $4\pi/3$; $5\pi/4$; $3\pi/2$; $7\pi/8$; $7\pi/4$; 3π.

4. A pendulum 1 meter long swings through an angle of $\pi/12$. How long is the arc it sweeps out?

5. Without using a table, find the following trigonometric functions: $\sin 2\pi/3$; $\sin 3\pi/4$; $\cos (-\pi/2)$; $\cos 3\pi/2$; $\cos \pi$; $\sin 7\pi/6$; $\sin 4\pi/3$; $\cos 4\pi/3$; $\sin (-2\pi/3)$; $\sin 7\pi/4$; $\cos 7\pi/4$.

6. What is the angle of elevation of the sun when a tree 10 meters high casts a shadow 5 meters long?

7. What do the graphs of $|\sin x|$ and $|\cos x|$ look like?

8. On the same set of axes, plot the graphs of $\sin x$, $2 \sin x$, $3 \sin x$, $\sin^2 x$, $\sin 2x$, $\sin 3x$, for x between 0 and 4π. (Distinguish among the curves by using different colors or different thicknesses.)

9. Plot graphs of $\sin 3x$ and of $\sin 2\pi x$ for x between 0 and 2π. Can you say anything about the relationship between the multiplicative constants (3 and 2π, respectively) and the form of the graphs?

PART II

CALCULUS

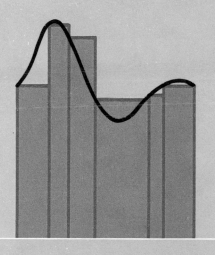

5

THE DEFINITE
INTEGRAL

1. THE NATURE OF THE PROBLEM

Although scientists are often concerned with states of equilibrium—i.e., with systems that do not change with time—the main subject matter of science is the nature of the *change* that we observe. The single most obvious feature of the physical world is the endless flux it is in, the endless changes of state that take place as time goes on. To the degree to which the scientist is successful in explaining *change*, he will succeed in comprehending most of what there is to know about nature.

There is nothing simple about static systems, even though the mathematics needed to cope with such systems is relatively elementary. As soon as we extend our study to systems undergoing change, the complexity increases infinitely, in a quite literal sense. Not only are the factors that must be taken into account far more numerous and varied, but the very description of these factors requires a mathematics capable of dealing with change of all sorts.

Attempts to develop such a mathematics surely go back to very early times and are in clear evidence in the writings of ancient Greek mathematicians, notably Archimedes. Eventually these attempts—increasingly numerous and successful as time went on—culminated in the development by Newton and Leibnitz (apparently independently) of a branch of mathematics known as calculus.[1]

Although Newton and Leibnitz built on broad and solid foundations constructed by their predecessors, they were the ones who gave the subject coherence and tied together its various parts. Their efforts in turn were followed by those of many eminent mathematicians who have continued to advance the field up to the present day.

There are two basic—and, as it turns out, related—problems whose solutions are necessary to a full description of change. One is the problem of *adding* quantities that vary continuously, in order to find the net sum of these quantities taken together. The classic example of this problem is the calculation of the area of an arbitrary figure with smooth boundaries; to find the answer, we must add up the areas of the continuously changing parts of the figure. We will turn to this problem first, in this chapter; we know that it was considered in some detail by Archimedes, and it ultimately led to the concept of the *definite integral*[2] and to the development of the integral calculus. The other basic problem is calculating the *rate of change* of a continuously varying quantity, in order to find how rapidly the quantity is changing at

---

[1] For a highly readable history of calculus, see C. B. Boyer, *The History of the Calculus and Its Conceptual Development* (*The Concepts of the Calculus*) (New York: Dover, 1959).

[2] The name comes from the meaning of *integral*, i.e., composite, complete whole. See Boyer, *History of the Calculus*, pp. 67, 205, 206.

any given instant. The classic example of this problem is finding the tangent to a curve at any given point; once it is found, the tangent gives us an idea of how steep the curve is at the point in question—i.e., loosely speaking, how rapidly it is varying in height. This problem will be considered in the next chapter; we know it was studied intensively by fourteenth-century mathematicians at Oxford, and it ultimately led to the concept of the *derivative*[3] and to the development of the differential calculus. Among other things, Newton and Leibnitz made the very important contribution of finding a relation between these two problems and thus linking together the integral and differential calculus. The nature of the relation will be studied in Chapter 7. That chapter is followed by some further developments and applications that are of general use in first courses in science.

2. A WORD OF CAUTION TO THE READER

In calculus, as in all branches of science and mathematics, there is a considerable distance between the intuitive basis of concepts and their formal, rigorous, formulation. While it is often the case that the more refined account retains many evident features of its heuristic foundations, with calculus this is less so. Calculus is based intuitively on an imprecise but highly vivid and pictorial idea, that of the *infinitesimal quantity*—a quantity that is, so to speak, infinitely small, but not vanishing. Attempts to clarify this idea and make it serviceable as the basis for an unambiguous, logically sound branch of mathematics met with repeated failure; the idea was struggled with for hundreds of years and was not dealt with more successfully by Newton and

[3] The origin of the name with Lagrange is somewhat complicated; see Boyer, *History of the Calculus*, pp. 252–254. Other names were also used for this concept until relatively recent times.

Leibnitz than by their predecessors. Concerning Newton's attempts, the astute critic Bishop Berkeley wrote—in one of many attacks:

> I have said (and I venture still to say) that . . . it is not possible to conceive a simple infinitesimal: that it is yet less possible to conceive an infinitesimal of an infinitesimal, and so onward. What have you to say in answer to this? Do you attempt to clear up the notion of [an infinitesimal]? Nothing like it.[4]

The criticisms of Berkeley and others sympathetic to his views ultimately bore fruit in a complete reformulation of the foundations of calculus. But this took much time and effort, and for over a century mathematicians tried to lend credibility and soundness to the infinitesimal. The French engineer, mathematician, and politician Lazare Carnot wrote an extremely popular book in 1797 summarizing all the notable formulations up to his time;[5] he concluded that, despite the obvious success of calculus as a tool in science and mathematics, the foundations of calculus were not satisfactorily constructed.

The work of the French mathematician Cauchy in the 1820's turned the tide, replacing propositions involving infinities and infinitesimals with propositions of a more abstract, less pictorial nature but possessing the precision necessary to a workable mathematics. Cauchy's work has been expanded upon and developed ever since, with the result that presentday calculus, resting on a firmer foundation, is capable of dealing confidently

---

[4] *A Defence of Free-Thinking in Mathematics. In Answer to a Pamphlet of Philalethes Cantabrigiensis* . . . *Also an Appendix concerning Mr. Walton's Vindication* . . . By the Author of "The Minute Philosopher" (i.e., by Bishop Berkeley). (Dublin, 1735), paragraph 17.

[5] L. N. M. Carnot, *Réflexions sur la Métaphysique du Calcul Infinitésimal* (Paris, Courcier: 1813). See also the colorful biography of Carnot in F. Arago, *Biographies of Distinguished Scientific Men*, English translation (2nd series, Boston: Ticknor Fields, 1859), pp. 1–116.

with problems and situations inaccessible to the intuitive methods in use before Cauchy's time.

It must be emphasized that the new formulation of calculus, as well as of *all* other branches of mathematics, that took place in the nineteenth century, far from being a sterile axiomatization and formalization, actually made possible an unbelievably rich flourishing in all extant fields of mathematical study and the opening of many entirely new fields. The elegance of nineteenth-century mathematical thought was no picayune preoccupation with unimportant details; it was rather an emancipation from the limitations imposed by imprecise concepts—limitations more severe in mathematics and logic than in any other branch of thought.

We shall restrict ourselves in this book to an exposition of the intuitive basis of calculus, leaning heavily on the infinitesimal. We do this because the intuitive basis is easy to grasp and easy to visualize; because it suffices in practice for all the purposes of introductory science courses; and because it serves even today to *guide* mathematicians in their highly successful efforts to extend and enrich calculus and to provide them with the pictorial image that seems to be so important a component of mathematical creativity. But we cannot sufficiently stress that our intuitive formulation is lacking in rigor by modern standards, that it is insufficient not only for the purposes of more advanced calculus but also for the purposes of more advanced scientific work, and that it uses modes of expression and thought which must always be used with care if errors are to be avoided. We are presenting this intuitive approach in order to make the material easily accessible to everyone and, even more important, to arouse the interest of the reader and make it possible and attractive for him to go on to study the modern formulation of calculus in all its richness and beauty.[6]

[6] An interesting introductory textbook in calculus is *First Course in Calculus* by S. Lang (Reading: Addison Wesley, 1964).

3. THE PROBLEM OF AREA. THE GEOMETRICAL DEFINITION OF THE DEFINITE INTEGRAL

When we ask to know the area of a plane figure (to which we shall restrict ourselves for the time being), we wish to know how much surface is enclosed by the figure's boundaries. In order to provide an answer, we must first agree on a basic unit of area, in terms of which all other areas can be expressed as numerical multiples. In the MKS (meter-kilogram-second) system, the unit of area is the *square meter* (meter^2), which is the area enclosed by a square measuring 1 meter on a side (see Fig. 5-1(a)). The area of a square of arbitrary size is found by measuring the number of square meters in the given square—and similarly for a rectangle. As was noted in Chapter 1, it is shown in elementary geometry that the number of square units in a rectangle of length l and width w is wl square units (see Fig. 5-1(b) and (c)). This also

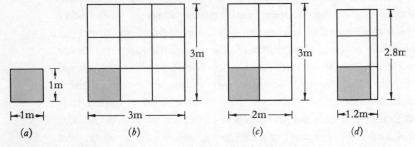

Fig. 5-1   (a) Unit area. (b) Area of a square 3m on a side. In terms of the unit area, the area is seen to be $9m^2 = 3m \times 3m$. (c) Area of a rectangle $2m \times 3m$. $A = 6m^2 = 2m \times 3m$. (d) Area of a rectangle $2.8m \times 1.2m$. $A = 3.36m^2 = 2.8m \times 1.2m$.

holds when w and l are not integers, in which case a nonintegral area may result (as in Fig. 5-1(d)).

There is thus no difficulty in ascertaining the area of a rectangular plane figure or of a right triangular plane figure (since its area is half the area of the rectangle determined by the base and altitude). Nor is there difficulty in finding the area of any plane figure, so long as the boundaries of the figure are made up of straight-line segments; this is because all such figures can be broken up into rectangular and right triangular parts, each of whose areas is easily found, and the area of the whole is then just the sum of the areas of the parts (Fig. 5-2).

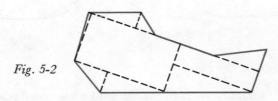

Fig. 5-2

Difficulty is encountered only when we deal with figures bounded by curved lines. The problem of finding how many units of area (i.e., how many unit squares) are contained in a figure with an arbitrary boundary is called the problem of *quadratures* (from the Latin word for square); the most famous such problem, which long occupied the attention of mathematicians for one reason or another, is the problem of finding the area of a circular disc (often called the problem of "squaring the circle"). To understand the way this problem finally was solved, it is useful to turn to practical methods of solving similar problems in everyday life. Suppose someone offered to sell land cheaply, at $5 per acre, and a buyer proposed to take an irregular plot a few acres in size that looked something like (*a*) in Fig. 5-3. Since not too much is at stake, both buyer and seller would doubtless agree to determine the area of the plot by dividing it into component parts somewhat as in Fig. 5-3(*b*), assuming for the sake of simplicity that the small segments left over (after the main rectangular segments at the center had been marked off) *could be approximated by straight-line boundaries*. In such a way, at little surveying cost, an estimate of size could be reached that

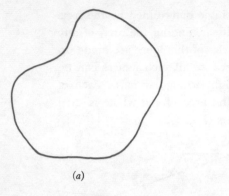

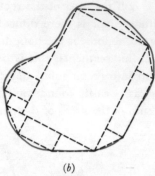

(a)   (b)

Fig. 5-3

would surely not be more than a few cents' worth off, considering the low selling price.

Suppose, however, we were dealing with a plot of land in the heart of New York City, selling for $100 per *square foot*. Obviously, crude methods would not do here. A plot looking like Fig. 5-4(a) would not only be subdivided into gross sections as in (b), but each left-over irregular boundary section would be further subdivided as in (c), until the left-over areas were of the order of *inches* in perimeter, at which juncture one could again approximate the curved sections by straight lines at no considerable loss.

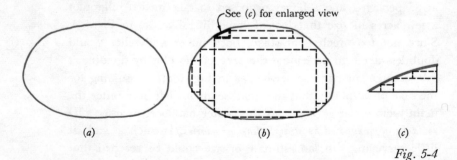

See (c) for enlarged view

(a)   (b)   (c)

Fig. 5-4

And so it would go in any practical situation. Depending on how important it was to us to be precise, we would use a finer and finer *grid* to subdivide the figure into rectangles, always ending by approximating the left-over sections by straight-edged areas. Indeed, if the grid were made fine enough (as Fig. 5-4(*c*) suggests), we might get enough of the area included in rectangular sections to be able to disregard entirely the little bit left over between the rectangles and the curved boundary.

This suggests that the finer we make the grid, the closer we get to the actual area of the figure. Intuitively, we might expect that if we let the grid become "infinitely" fine, *nothing* would be left over, and we would have an exact answer. This intuitive suggestion lies at the heart of the concept of the *definite integral*, as the exact area is called, and we shall now elaborate on it a bit. We shall limit ourselves for the present to figures bounded by three straight mutually perpendicular lines and by a fourth arbitrarily curved side. This simplifies the discussion with no loss of generality, since any figure can be subdivided into segments such that the left-over pieces near the boundary have the shape under consideration.[7]

Consider, then, Fig. 5-5(*a*). Our discussion would seem to indicate that in order to get a very crude idea of its area, we can subdivide it as shown in (*b*) and restrict ourselves to the sum of the rectangular areas, neglecting the left-over sections; in order to get a better idea of the area, we can subdivide it as in (*c*) and add the rectangular areas; and in order to do even better, we need only subdivide it more finely. Furthermore, we find the numerical results we obtain by adding the rectangular areas get closer and closer to the numerical magnitude of the actual area and there-

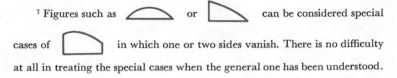

[7] Figures such as ⟨image⟩ or ⟨image⟩ can be considered special cases of ⟨image⟩ in which one or two sides vanish. There is no difficulty at all in treating the special cases when the general one has been understood.

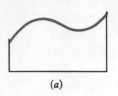
(a)

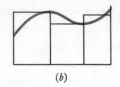
(b)

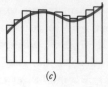
(c)

Fig. 5-5

fore *differ from each other less and less* as we subdivide more finely. Roughly speaking, we expect that the sum of the rectangular areas will approach the actual area as a *limiting value* when the subdivision approaches infinitely fine rectangles as a limiting subdivision.

We have seen that in practice we can always add up the sum as long as we have a finite number of strips, and that in practice we carry out the limiting process only as far as we feel necessary in order not to suffer undue loss by neglecting what is left over. It is not at all clear how the final limit of infinite sub-division can actually be *evaluated* (and not only spoken about!). Indeed, as long as we restrict ourselves to the geometric language of this section, the value of the limit cannot be written down in general terms and can be found only with great ingenuity in particular cases where the curved boundary has certain specified shapes. Only when we translate our geometric discussion into algebraic terms can a practical general formulation be presented with ease, and it is in large measure due to this fact that the development of calculus leaped forward only after analytic geometry came into general use.

We shall now express our results in algebraic language.

4. THE PROBLEM OF AREA. THE ALGEBRAIC DEFINITION OF THE DEFINITE INTEGRAL

Let us return to the plane figure shown in Fig. 5-5(a), this time drawn on a plane containing (x,y) coordinate axes (see Fig. 5-6). For simplicity, we shall place the base of the figure on the positive x-axis. The outline of the figure can now be described

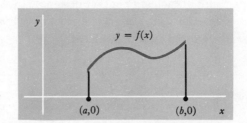

Fig. 5-6

by equations which, when plotted, yield the boundaries. Thus, the base (a straight line) is described by the linear equation $y = 0$ (the equation of the x-axis). The left side, a vertical straight line passing through some point on the axis—having, say, coordinates $(a,0)$—is described by the equation $x = a$. The right side, passing through $(b,0)$, is described by $x = b$. (The values of a and b depend on the problem at hand, i.e., on the width of the figure being considered. We leave them arbitrary for the purposes of this general discussion.) The upper boundary, according to the problem we have agreed to consider, is some arbitrary curve, the graph of some functional relationship between x and y; we will designate this relationship by the general notation $y = f(x)$, understanding that in any particular problem the particular function whose graph is the upper boundary must be known before we can proceed with the calculation.[8]

---

[8] The reader may wonder whether one can always find a function whose graph will yield the arbitrary curved boundary with which one starts. A moment's reflection shows the answer to be yes. The function can be constructed by reading off the coordinates of the points through which the

Our geometric problem has thus been translated into the following algebraic one: Find the area lying between the curve $y = f(x)$ and the x-axis in the interval $x = a$ to $x = b$. This area is called "the definite integral of $y = f(x)$ from a to b."

We are now ready to formulate our geometrical prescription for finding the integral in algebraic language. We divide the interval from a to b into some number (n) of equal segments; the width of each segment we designate by Δx (read "delta x"). Thus, since the width of each segment is $(1/n)^{\text{th}}$ the width $(b - a)$ of the entire interval, we have

$$\Delta x = (b - a)/n \tag{5-1}$$

These segments form the bases of the rectangular strips with which we approximate the area. The height of each rectangle will be taken to be the height of the curve at the left-hand side of the strip (see Fig. 5-7).

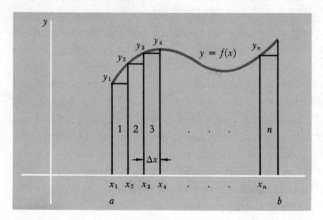

Fig. 5-7

chosen curve passes. The list of coordinate pairs is the function being sought, since the list gives immediately the value of y associated with each value of x. In practice, we shall deal with boundary curves whose equations are relatively simple—e.g., $y = x^2$.

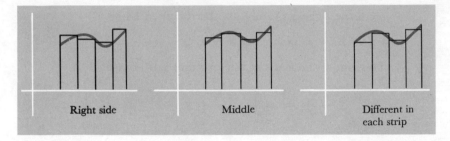

Fig. 5-8

A word is in order about the numerous seemingly arbitrary choices we have been making. For example, we took all strips to be of equal width Δx, whereas our original geometrical discussion nowhere stipulated that they be of equal width. In fact, they need not be, and our choice was made for the sake of calculational convenience; the result comes out the same whether they are equal or not, *when we go to the limit of infinite subdivision*, provided only that all strips shrink to infinitesimal width so that no finite-sized strips remain. Similarly, the choice to make the height of the strips equal to the height of the curve at their left side is arbitrary. We could have chosen the height at the right side or in the middle or at any other point or even at different points in different strips (see Fig. 5-8)—the result would have come out the same in the limit of infinite subdivision, since in that limit each strip is infinitely narrow and has the same height on the right side, the left side, and throughout the intervening infinitesimal interval.

Returning now to our particularly simple choice, illustrated in Fig. 5-7, we see that the area of the first strip is given by the product of height and base. Designating the height of the curve at the left side of the first rectangle (i.e., at $x = a$) by y_1, we have

$$A_1 = y_1 \, \Delta x \qquad\qquad (5\text{-}2)$$

Similarly, for the second rectangle, $A_2 = y_2 \, \Delta x$, and for the ith

rectangle (where i is any number between 1 and n):

$$A_i = y_i \Delta x \qquad 1 \leqq i \leqq n \tag{5-3}$$

The sum of the areas of the n rectangular strips is thus

$$S_n = A_1 + A_2 + \cdots + A_n = \sum_{i=1}^{n} A_i = y_1 \Delta x$$

$$+ \cdots + y_n \Delta x = \sum_{i=1}^{n} y_i \Delta x \tag{5-4}$$

Another way of writing this is the following: If we denote, as in Fig. 5-7, the x coordinates of the left sides of the strips by x_1, x_2, . . . , x_n, then since $y = f(x)$ holds for all points on the curve, we have $y_1 = f(x_1)$, $y_2 = f(x_2)$, etc. In other words, another way of writing the height y_i is $f(x_i)$, so that

$$S_n = f(x_1) \Delta x + \cdots + f(x_n) \Delta x = \sum_{i=1}^{n} f(x_i) \Delta x \tag{5-5}$$

We are now ready to pass to the limit of infinitely fine subdivision. What we have said is that the actual area is obtained by making each strip infinitesimally small in width or, what is the same, by letting the number of subdivisions approach infinity. To express this in standard mathematical notation, we introduce the following notations: "A" designates the actual area; "$\int$" designates the definite integral (this sign is a modified S—for "Sum"—first introduced by Leibnitz); "lim" designates the limit, with the nature of the limit written underneath. Using these notations, we can write:

$$\left. \begin{array}{l} A \equiv \displaystyle\int_a^b y \, dx \;\; = \lim_{n \to \infty} \sum_{i=1}^{n} y_i \Delta x \\[4mm] A \equiv \displaystyle\int_a^b f(x) \, dx = \lim_{n \to \infty} \sum_{i=1}^{n} f(x_i) \Delta x \end{array} \right\} \tag{5-6}$$

A few other notational points should be mentioned. The subscript a and superscript b to the integral sign denote the "limits of integration"—i.e., the left and right boundaries, respectively, of the area being considered; the product immediately to the right of the integral sign (either $f(x)\,dx$ or $y\,dx$) is called *the integrand* and is supposed to bring to mind the nature of the summation being performed—a summation of strip areas, each being the product of a height (y, or $f(x)$) and an infinitesimally narrow base dx. This is our first introduction of the "d" notation: "Δ" always refers to finite intervals, "d" to infinitesimal ones, i.e., to intervals left after passage to the limit.

This completes the algebraic definition of the integral. At this point it is by no means clear that Eq. 5-6 is an improvement, for calculational purposes, over the geometrical description of the previous section. That this is so will appear clearly in the next section, where we will proceed to our first quantitative calculations of actual areas.

5. SOME SPECIFIC DEFINITE INTEGRALS

We shall begin by applying our definition to cases where the answers are known in advance, in order to develop insight into the way integration works. Consider a rectangle one unit high and $(b - a)$ units long (see Fig. 5-9). We know that its area is simply $1 \cdot (b - a) = (b - a)$ square units. Let us see how our definition of the definite integral gives us this answer.

We divide the figure into n strips, of width Δx given by Eq. 5-1. According to Eq. 5-6, the area is

$$A = \lim_{n \to \infty} \sum_{i=1}^{n} f(x_i)\,\Delta x$$

where $f(x_i)$ is the height of each strip, i.e., the height of the upper

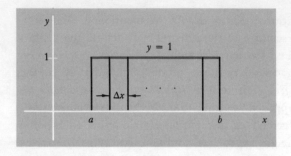

Fig. 5-9

bounding curve at the left side of the strip. In this case, the height does not vary at all from strip to strip, but remains always one unit. Thus, here

$$f(x_i) = 1 \qquad \text{for all } i \tag{5-7}$$

The sum thus becomes

$$\sum_{i=1}^{n} 1 \cdot \Delta x$$

i.e., the sum of n terms, each of which is the same. This sum is easily evaluated to be

$$\sum_{i=1}^{n} 1 \cdot \Delta x = n \, \Delta x \tag{5-8}$$

We can now evaluate the integral, using Eq. 5-1:

$$A = \lim_{n \to \infty} \sum_{i=1}^{n} 1 \cdot \Delta x = \lim_{n \to \infty} n \, \Delta x = \lim_{n \to \infty} \frac{n(b-a)}{n}$$
$$= \lim_{n \to \infty} (b-a) = (b-a) \tag{5-9}$$

The last step, passing to the limit $n \to \infty$, was easy in this case, since $(b-a)$ did not involve n at all—i.e., the result did not depend at all on the number of strips, since we are dealing with a rectangle. The limiting process thus gives with no difficulty the result we expected, and we can thus write our first integration formula for the special case where the upper bounding curve is $y = 1$:

$$\int_a^b 1 \cdot dx = \int_a^b dx = (b - a) \tag{5-10}$$

We now proceed to a slightly more complicated case, where the upper curve is still a straight line, but inclined to the x-axis. For simplicity, we choose the upper boundary to be the curve $y = x$, whose slope is 1 and whose angle of inclination is therefore $\pi/4$ (45°; tan 45° = 1). (See Fig. 5-10.) The area is easily found

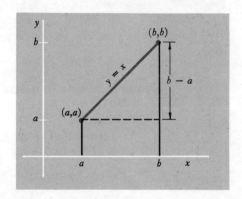

Fig. 5-10

by elementary geometry: The figure is a trapezoid, and its area is the sum of the areas of the rectangular part and the triangular part:

$$\begin{aligned}
A &= a(b - a) + (\tfrac{1}{2})(b - a)(b - a) \\
&= ab - a^2 + (\tfrac{1}{2})b^2 - ab + (\tfrac{1}{2})a^2 \\
&= (\tfrac{1}{2})(b^2 - a^2)
\end{aligned} \tag{5-11}$$

Let us see how our rules for integration give the same answer. We divide the figure into n strips, each of width Δx (see Fig. 5-11). The upper curve is given by $y = x$, and this enables us to find the strip heights y_i; they are simply equal to the values of the x-coordinates at the left boundaries of the strips. Thus, the first

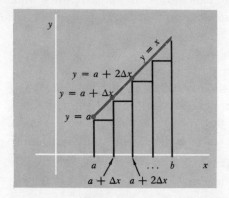

Fig. 5-11

strip height is $y_1 = a$, the second is $y_2 = a + \Delta x$, etc. The sum is thus

$$\sum_{i=1}^{n} y_i \, \Delta x = a \, \Delta x + [a + \Delta x] \, \Delta x + [a + 2 \, \Delta x] \, \Delta x$$
$$+ \cdots + [a + (n - 1) \, \Delta x] \, \Delta x$$
$$= a \, \Delta x + a \, \Delta x + \Delta x \, \Delta x + a \, \Delta x + 2 \, \Delta x \, \Delta x$$
$$+ \cdots + a \, \Delta x + (n - 1) \, \Delta x \, \Delta x$$
$$= n[a \, \Delta x] + \Delta x[\Delta x + 2 \, \Delta x + \cdots + (n - 1) \, \Delta x]$$
$$= na \, \Delta x + [\Delta x]^2[1 + 2 + 3$$
$$+ \cdots + (n - 1)] \qquad (5\text{-}12)$$

According to Chapter 2, Eq. 2-27, the sum of integers in Eq. 5-12 is given by

$$1 + 2 + 3 + \cdots + (n - 1) = n \, (n - 1)/2$$

This enables us to write

$$\sum_{i=1}^{n} y_i \, \Delta x = na \, \Delta x + (\Delta x)^2 n(n - 1)/2 \qquad (5\text{-}13)$$

Using Eq. 5-1, this becomes

$$\sum_{i=1}^{n} y_i \, \Delta x = na(b - a)/n + (\tfrac{1}{2})[(b - a)^2/n^2](n^2 - n)$$

$$= a(b - a) + (\tfrac{1}{2})(b - a)^2(1 - 1/n) \qquad (5\text{-}14)$$

We can now evaluate the integral for our case $y = x$:

$$\int_a^b x \, dx = \lim_{n \to \infty} \sum_{i=1}^{n} y_i \, \Delta x$$

$$= \lim_{n \to \infty} \{a(b - a) + (\tfrac{1}{2})(b - a)^2(1 - 1/n)\}$$

$$(5\text{-}15)$$

Now, the only term containing n in the brackets is $(1 - 1/n)$, so this is the only term affected by passage to the limit $n \to \infty$. As n gets larger, $1/n$ gets smaller, so that the difference $1 - 1/n$ gets closer and closer to being simply 1; in the limit $n \to \infty$, $1 - 1/n \to 1$, so that we can write

$$\int_a^b x \, dx = a(b - a) + (\tfrac{1}{2})(b - a)^2 = (\tfrac{1}{2})(b^2 - a^2)$$

$$(5\text{-}16)$$

which is just the answer we expected, according to Eq. 5-11.

Now that we have some practice in the methods of integration, we can proceed to unfamiliar examples. Consider the figure bounded by the curve $y = x^2$ (known as a parabola, and shown in Fig. 5-12). Here, for the first time, we are faced with calculating exactly an area not bounded by straight line segments. We divide it into n strips, each of width Δx, and note as before that the x-coordinates of the left-hand side of these strips are given by $x_1 = a$, $x_2 = a + \Delta x$, $x_3 = a + 2 \, \Delta x$, . . . , $x_n = a + (n - 1)\Delta x$. The functional relationship between y and x, $y = x^2$, that describes the upper curve provides us with the respective heights of the strips, namely, $y_1 = a^2$, $y_2 = (a + \Delta x)^2$, $y_3 = (a + 2 \, \Delta x)^2$, . . . , $y_n = [a + (n - 1) \, \Delta x]^2$. This in turn

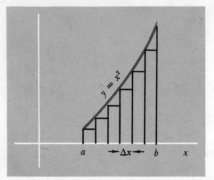

Fig. 5-12

enables us to form the sum:

$$\sum_{i=1}^{n} y_i \, \Delta x = a^2 \, \Delta x + (a + \Delta x)^2 \, \Delta x + (a + 2 \, \Delta x)^2 \, \Delta x$$
$$+ \cdots + [a + (n - 1) \, \Delta x]^2 \, \Delta x$$
$$= a^2 \, \Delta x + [a^2 + 2a \, \Delta x + \Delta x^2] \, \Delta x$$
$$+ [a^2 + 4a \, \Delta x + 4 \, \Delta x^2] \, \Delta x + \cdots$$
$$+ [a^2 + 2a(n - 1) \, \Delta x + (n - 1)^2 \, \Delta x^2] \, \Delta x$$
$$= na^2 \, \Delta x + a(2 \, \Delta x) \, \Delta x + a(4 \, \Delta x) \, \Delta x + \cdots$$
$$+ 2a[(n - 1) \, \Delta x] \, \Delta x + (\Delta x^2) \, \Delta x + (4 \, \Delta x^2) \, \Delta x$$
$$+ \cdots + (n - 1)^2 (\Delta x^2) \, \Delta x$$
$$= na^2 \, \Delta x + 2 \, \Delta x^2 a[1 + 2 + \cdots + (n - 1)]$$
$$+ \Delta x^3 [1^2 + 2^2 + \cdots + (n - 1)^2]$$
$$(5\text{-}17)$$

The sum in the first square brackets is the one we have just encountered, and that in the second square brackets can be evaluated, using the algebra of progressions:

$$1^2 + 2^2 + \cdots + (n - 1)^2 = (n - 1)n(2n - 1)/6$$
$$= \frac{2n^3 - 3n^2 + n}{6} \quad (5\text{-}18)^9$$

---

[9] See, e.g., R. Courant and H. Robbins, *What is Mathematics?* (4th ed., New York: Oxford, 1960), p. 14.

Using Eq. 5-1, the sum becomes

$$\sum_{i=1}^{n} y_i\,\Delta x = na^2(b-a)/n + 2a[(b-a)^2/n^2][(n^2-n)/2]$$
$$+ [(b-a)^3/n^3][2n^3 - 3n^2 + n/6]\ .$$
$$= a^2(b-a) + (b-a)^2a(1-1/n)$$
$$+ (\tfrac{1}{6})(b-a)^3(2-3/n+1/n^2) \qquad (5\text{-}19)$$

We can now pass to the limit $n \to \infty$ in Eq. 5-19 in order to find the integral. We have already seen that the limit of $(1 - 1/n)$ as $n \to \infty$ is 1; by the same arguments, the limit of $(2 - 3/n + 1/n^2)$ as $n \to \infty$ is 2. Thus

$$\int_a^b x^2\,dx = \lim_{n\to\infty} \sum_{i=1}^{n} y_i\,\Delta x = a^2(b-a) + a(b-a)^2$$
$$+ \tfrac{1}{3}(b-a)^3$$
$$= a^2b - a^3 + ab^2 - 2a^2b + a^3 + (\tfrac{1}{3})b^3$$
$$- b^2a + ba^2 - (\tfrac{1}{3})a^3$$
$$= (\tfrac{1}{3})(b^3 - a^3) \qquad (5\text{-}20)$$

If we collect the formulas we have derived, a pattern will be seen to emerge. Recalling that $x^0 = 1$, we can rewrite Eq. 5-10 so that Eqs. 5-10, 5-16, and 5-20 are:

$$\int_a^b x^0\,dx = \quad (b-a)$$
$$\int_a^b x\ \,dx = (\tfrac{1}{2})(b^2-a^2)$$
$$\int_a^b x^2\,dx = (\tfrac{1}{3})(b^3-a^3) \qquad (5\text{-}21)$$

On the basis of Eq. 5-21, we would guess that

$$\int_a^b x^3\,dx = (\tfrac{1}{4})(b^4-a^4)$$

or, in other words, that

$$\int_a^b x^n\,dx = \frac{1}{n+1}\,(b^{n+1} - a^{n+1}) \qquad (5\text{-}22)$$

This turns out to be the case, and not only for n as a positive integer, but for n as *any* real number, positive or negative, integral, rational, or irrational (except for $n = -1$, where the right-hand side of Eq. 5-22 becomes meaningless; this single exception will later be seen to be quite significant). The proof of Eq. 5-22 for all n ($n \neq -1$) can be found in most standard calculus textbooks. With the aid of Eq. 5-22 we can calculate the areas of all figures whose upper boundaries can be described by an equation of the form $y = x^n$, where n is any real number ($n \neq -1$).

The methods of integral calculus have thus enabled us to calculate one class of areas previously inaccessible to calculation. Many more examples will be added in succeeding chapters.

Before closing this section, we shall introduce another notational innovation. In all the integrals appearing in Eqs. 5-21 and 5-22 we see that the right-hand side involves a difference of two terms, identical in form and differing only in that the left-hand limit a replaces the right-hand limit b in the negative term. (Because of their positions relative to the integral sign, a and b are usually referred to as "lower" and "upper" limits, respectively.) The following shorthand notation is introduced to designate this difference:

$$x \Big|_a^b \quad \textit{means} \text{ "evaluate } x \text{ at } b \text{ and subtract from it the value of } x \text{ at } a\text{"—i.e., means } (b - a)$$

$$x^2 \Big|_a^b \quad \textit{means} \text{ "evaluate } x^2 \text{ at } b \text{ and subtract from it the value of } x^2 \text{ at } a\text{"—i.e., means } (b^2 - a^2)$$

$$x^n \Big|_a^b \quad \textit{means} \text{ "evaluate } x^n \text{ at } b \text{ and subtract from it the value of } x^n \text{ at } a\text{"—i.e., means } (b^n - a^n)$$

and, in general, for any function of x, $f(x)$:

$$f(x) \Big|_a^b \quad \textit{means} \text{ "evaluate } f(x) \text{ at } b \text{ and subtract from it the value of } f(x) \text{ at } a\text{"—i.e., means } f(b) - f(a)$$

$$(5\text{-}23)$$

Using this notation, Eq. 5-22 can be written:

$$\int_{a}^{b} x^n \, dx = \frac{x^{n+1}}{n+1} \Big|_{a}^{b} \quad (n \neq -1) \tag{5-24}$$

6. SOME RULES OF INTEGRATION

With the aid of either the geometric or algebraic definitions of the definite integral, we can derive some rules of integration that greatly simplify actual calculations.

Suppose we know the area under one curve and we want to know the area under another *twice as high*—i.e., under another curve whose y-coordinates are everywhere twice the y-coordinates of the original curve. Since the heights of all strips in the latter case will be double the heights in the former case, the strip areas will also be double the former areas; the net area will therefore also be twice as large (Fig. 5-13). In terms of integrals, this means that

$$\int_{a}^{b} 2f(x) \, dx = 2 \int_{a}^{b} f(x) \, dx$$

In general, the area under a curve that is c times as high as a given curve will be c times the area under the given curve, where

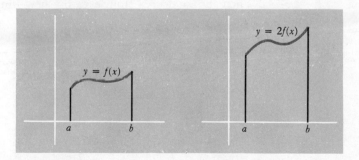

Fig. 5-13

c is any number:

$$\int_a^b cf(x) \; dx = c \int_a^b f(x) \; dx \tag{5-25}$$

We could just as well have chosen to proceed from right to left in finding the area, instead of going from left to right. In going from right to left (i.e., starting at the right boundary and adding up the areas of the strips successively until the left boundary is reached) we must remember, however, that we are proceeding in the direction of *decreasing* x values, so that successive x values from right to left get smaller. This means that the Δx's [which are now equal to $(a - b)/n$] are negative instead of positive; otherwise, everything is the same as going from left to right. Stated in symbols, this tells us that

$$\int_a^b f(x) \; dx = - \int_b^a f(x) \; dx \tag{5-26}$$

In other words, switching upper and lower limits changes the sign of the integral.

Suppose we decide to calculate an additional area under a given curve, beyond the limit b originally decided upon; suppose we wish to calculate the area from b to some new limit c (Fig. 5-14). Then the total area from a to the new limit c is just the

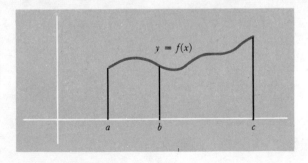

$y = f(x)$

a b c

Fig. 5-14

sum of the area from a to b plus the additional area from b to c:

$$\int_a^b f(x)\,dx + \int_b^c f(x)\,dx = \int_a^c f(x)\,dx \qquad (5\text{-}27)$$

Our last rule concerns the sum of two different integrals evaluated between the same two limits. Each integral represents the area under a particular curve and between the two limits. Thus, if one curve is described by the functional relationship $y = f(x)$, and the other by $y = g(x)$, the areas in question are represented by

$$\int_a^b f(x)\,dx \qquad \text{and} \qquad \int_a^b g(x)\,dx$$

respectively (see Fig. 5-15), and the sum of these integrals is

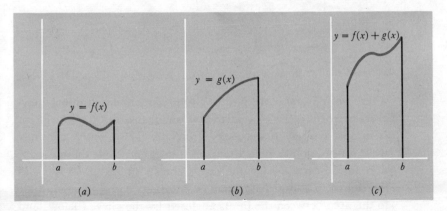

Fig. 5-15

just the sum of the areas. Suppose, now, that we consider a third curve whose height at each value of x is given by $[f(x) + g(x)]$. If we calculate the area under the third curve between the same limits, we find that the strips have heights equal to the sum of the strip heights of the separate curves, while the bases are the same $[\Delta x = (b - a)/n]$. The strip areas in the third case will thus be the sum of the strip areas in the separate integrals, so that the total area will be the sum of the separate areas:

$$\int_a^b f(x)\,dx + \int_a^b g(x)\,dx = \int_a^b [f(x) + g(x)]\,dx \quad (5\text{-}28)$$

Note that, by contrast to earlier rules, the rule given in Eq. 5-28 is not obvious when studied visually, in its geometrical representation.

We have been assuming all along that the figure in question lies in the first (i.e., upper-right hand) quadrant of the x-y plane,

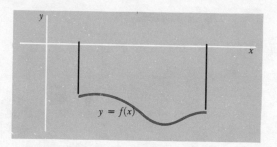

Fig. 5-16

where both x and y are positive. Our algebraic definition, however, nowhere refers to a particular quadrant, and the restriction is in fact entirely unnecessary—as long as we watch carefully what we are doing. We can, for example, carry out the prescription for integration for the curve shown in Fig. 5-16 lying in the fourth quadrant; the result will still be equal in magnitude to the area between the limits enclosed by the curve (below) and the x-axis (above). The only difference will be that the result will come out with a minus sign, since the values of y will be negative. Thus, in this case the definite integral will not give the area directly, but will give the negative of the area. In general, the integration procedure, if applied to arbitrary curves in the xy-plane, has to be examined with respect to the sign of the answer. In cases such as Fig. 5-16 the sign is negative and the value of the integral is minus the area. In cases such as Fig. 5-17, where the curve changes quadrants, the portion in each quadrant must be handled separately if the total area is desired. Integration from a to b in such cases may even yield *zero* as an answer, although the net area is obviously not vanishing; to find the area

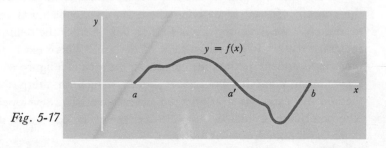

Fig. 5-17

the integration must be performed separately from a to a', then from a' to b, and the sign taken into account.

Finally, we might note explicitly the obvious fact that, although we have been using y and x exclusively to denote the variables, all the results hold for any set of symbols used to denote the variables.

7. THE SOLUTION OF THE PROBLEM OF AREAS. RELATED PROBLEMS

Having come this far in our discussion of areas and integrals, we can now take stock and ask: To what extent have we in fact developed a method for finding the precise area of a figure enclosed by curved boundaries? The answer to this question depends on the meaning we attach to the word *area*. It appears at first sight—and our entire discussion has so far gone along with this appearance—that every figure has a *real* area, expressible quantitatively as so-many square units, and that the problem is only to find a way to measure this real area. We feel that our eyes tell us that there is such an area! Viewed this way, integration is taken to be a method for obtaining the numerical result desired.

The trouble is that whether or not we attach significance to the concept of *"real* area, lying there waiting to be measured accurately," we have no way of finding out whether the definite integral "really" is the magnitude of the area. There exists no other independent method for measuring the area of a figure with a continuously varying boundary; indeed, if such an alternative method did exist, integration need never have been developed. The point is that, just because all other means failed, a method involving infinite limits was devised.

This means that the definite integral is actually a *definition* of the precise area of a figure. The exact value of the magnitude of the area *is* the value of the integral. To be sure, we arrived at this definition of area through an intuitive feeling that this is the way it should be done; but, once the process of integration has been precisely specified, the result is that the integral, being the only expression available for the area, is therefore the defined value of the area, once and for all, by default.

The realization of this situation, which actually took some time, freed people from a maze of circular and unresolvable argumentation revolving around the question of whether the limiting process described in this chapter really measures all the area. In the absence of an alternative scheme generally acceptable to mathematicians, integration came to be taken as a definition of the area. Naturally, it was important to prove—as was done in Section 5—that the areas obtained by integration for figures bounded by straight lines agreed with the areas obtained for these figures by standard geometrical techniques. The new, more general definition thus reduces in the special cases to the old, more restricted definition.

Integrals have been described in this chapter solely in terms of areas, but the concept of the definite integral comes into play whenever we have to add the effects of changing quantities. In such situations the method of integration naturally suggests itself, and in such situations, as here, the definite integral arrived at through intuition serves as the definition of the sum in question. Whether the resulting quantity so defined is useful to science will, of course, depend on whether it is useful in describing experience.

EXERCISES

1. Draw a graph of the parabola $y = x^2$ between $x = 0$ and $x = 3$. (a) Find the area bounded by the parabola, the x-axis, and the lower and upper limits $x = 1$, $x = 3$, by *integration*.   (b) Slice the area into ten strips, each of width $\Delta x = 0.2$, and of heights equal to the value of y at the left-hand boundary of the strips. Find the areas of the strips and add them. Compare the result with (a). (c) Do the same as (b), using strips whose heights are the y values at the midpoints of the strips. (d) Same as (b), for strips whose heights are the y values at the right-hand boundaries.
2. Carry out the procedure of the previous problem for the functions $y = x$ and $y = x^3$.
3. Carry out the procedure of the previous problem for $y = 2x^2$; $y = x^2 + x^3$. Compare with the results expected from the rules of integration.
4. Consider the curve $y = f(x)$ shown in Fig. 5-18.

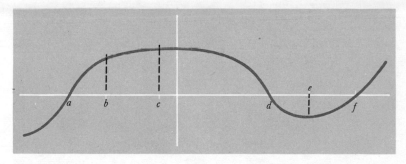

Fig. 5-18

Determine the signs of the following integrals: $\int_a^b f(x)\,dx$; $\int_c^d f(x)\,dx$; $\int_c^b f(x)\,dx$; $\int_e^c f(x)\,dx$; $\int_d^f f(x)\,dx$; $\int_a^f f(x)\,dx$.

5. Find the area bounded by the x-axis, the given curve, and the indicated limits: (a) $y = 4 - 3x^2$, between $x = -1$ and $x = 1$; (b) $y = x^{\frac{1}{2}}$, between $x = 0$ and $x = 9$; (c) $y = x^3 - x$, between $x = -1$ and $x = 1$.

6. Evaluate the following definite integrals: $4\int_1^2 ds$; $\int_1^2 (\frac{1}{2})t\,dt$; $\int_1^2 u(1 - u)\,du$; $\int_1^2 (3x^2 + 4x - 5)\,dx$; $\int_1^2 (v + 1)^2\,dv$; $\int_1^2 dy/y^2$; $\int_1^2 \frac{(w^2 - 2)}{w^2}\,dw$.

7. Find: $\int_1^8 (7t - 5 - t^2)\,dt$; $\int_{-a}^{+a} (a^2 - x^2)\,dx$.

8. Make a graph of the functions $f(x) = x^2$ and $g(x) = x + 1$ between $x = -\frac{1}{2}$ and $x = +\frac{3}{2}$. Shade the area *between* the curves and find the magnitude of this area by integration.

9. Find the value of the following integrals: $\int_{-1}^{+1} x\,dx$; $\int_{-1}^{+1} x^2\,dx$; $\int_{-1}^{+1} x^3\,dx$; $\int_{-1}^{+1} x^4 \cos^2 x \sin^5 x\,dx$.

10. Evaluate the following integrals: $\int_1^0 \sqrt{x}\,dx$; $\int_9^{16} dx/\sqrt{x}$; $\int_0^4 (2 - x^{\frac{1}{2}})^2\,dx$; $\int_8^0 (4 - y^2/16)^2\,dy$.

11. Sketch and evaluate the area enclosed by the two curves $y = 2x^2 + 1$ and $y = x^2 + 5$.

6

THE DERIVATIVE

1. THE PROBLEM OF TANGENTS. THE GEOMETRICAL DEFINITION OF THE DERIVATIVE

If we wish to find out "how steep" a curve is at any point (i.e., "where it is headed"), we draw the tangent to the curve at that point. Loosely speaking, the tangent to a curve at a point is the straight line that just touches the curve there, without actually intersecting it (Fig. 6-1).[1] The straight line so defined

[1] The tangent may intersect the curve at some other, distant point, as:

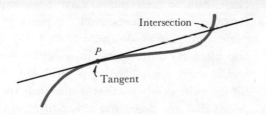

The important thing is that in order for it to qualify as a tangent at point P, it must not intersect the curve at that point, but only barely touch it there.

Fig. 6-1   (a) Tangent. (b) Secants.

has the same "direction" as the curve does at the point of contact: The line serves to display this direction on a large scale, since the difference between a straight line and a curve is just that the curve changes direction from point to point, whereas the line by definition has the same direction at all points (see Chapter 3, Section 4).

It is quite a trick to find the line that *just touches* the curve at the given point *P*, since it is not at all easy to distinguish this line, the true tangent, from other lines that are secants intersecting the curve at two points, the second lying very very near point *P*. For certain special curves it is possible with some ingenuity to find prescriptions for drawing the true tangent to a point. For example, we learn in Euclidean geometry that the tangent to a *circle* at any point is the line perpendicular to the radius from the center to that point. Since we know how to construct perpendiculars, we can always draw a tangent to a circle. Similar prescriptions have been found over the centuries for other special curves. Now, in practice, when we attempt to draw a tangent we do the following (Fig. 6-2): We take a ruler and place it on the curve, intersecting the curve at the point *P* and at another neighboring point. Using *P* as the pivot, we then tilt the ruler slowly, so that it intersects the curve at neighboring points that are closer and closer to *P*, until we finally reach an inclination such that we are satisfied the ruler no longer intersects the curve at all, but just touches it at *P*.

If we now abstract from our everyday experience the essence

of what we are doing, we can come up with a geometrical understanding of a tangent. To find the tangent to a curve at point P,
we first draw a secant intersecting the curve at point P and at
a second point O nearby, to the right of P. (Again, the choice of O
to the *right* of P is completely arbitrary, and the same result is
obtained for a point to the left of P in all cases with which we
shall be concerned.) We then draw successive secants through
points O', O'', O''', etc., each point in turn being closer to P
than its predecessor (see Fig. 6-3 (a) and (b)). At each stage the
line is well defined, since it passes through two prescribed points
and two points determine a line unequivocally. As the points
get closer to P, the secants get closer to the tangent and, indeed,
the secants *differ less and less in inclination from one another*. For the
practical purposes described in the preceding paragraph, the

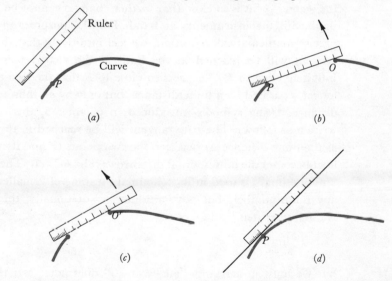

*Fig. 6-2   (a) Curve and ruler. Tangent at point P is to be found. (b)
Ruler placed on curve intersecting it at P and O. Ruler is then tilted slowly
in direction shown. (c) Ruler now intersects curve at O', closer to P. Tilt
still more. (d) Ruler now just touches at P. Tangent can be drawn.*

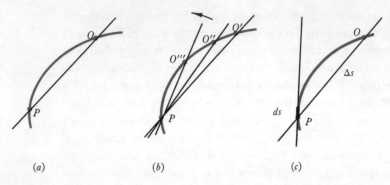

Fig. 6-3

difference between the true tangent and the secants through very near points is undetectable; this difference can be neglected once the second point is so close that further changes cannot be measured with the instruments at hand. For the purposes of more precise mathematical definition, we feel intuitively that the true tangent will be reached in the limit as the second point gets infinitely close to P—i.e., gets so close to P that the two are no longer separated by a finite distance, but only by an infinitesimal distance. Using symbols introduced in Chapter 5, this can be written as follows: The true tangent will be reached in the limit as the finite distance Δs between the two points (P and its neighbor) becomes the infinitesimal distance ds (Fig. 6-3 (c)). The word "infinitesimal" is used in its colloquial meaning of "smaller than any finite number, but not vanishing." Notationally, this limit is usually written

$$\text{"}\lim_{\Delta s \to 0}\text{"}$$

but we must understand that "$\Delta s \to 0$" does not mean that Δs is taken *equal* to 0, only that it *approaches* 0, becoming smaller than *any* given finite magnitude.

It is important when discussing tangents in this intuitive, pictorial way to realize that we must view the tangent at a point P

as actually passing through *two* points, *P and an infinitely close neighbor.* We might be tempted simply to say that the tangent is the limit of the secant as the second point becomes identical with *P*; but this would be an unfortunate way of phrasing the limit, since this would imply that in the limit the line would be determined by a single point, whereas, in fact, one point does not suffice to determine a line unambiguously. For this reason, we must say that in the limit there are still two points—thus keeping the line well defined even in the limit—but that in the limit these two points are infinitely close.

The geometrical definition of a tangent, at which we have now arrived, leads directly to the definition of the *derivative: The derivative of a curve at a point P is the slope of the tangent to the curve at P* (see Chapter 3, Section 4 and Fig. 6-4). Thus, the *derivative*

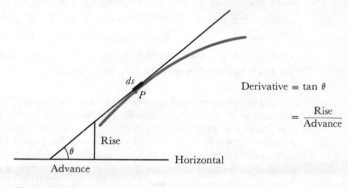

$$\text{Derivative} \equiv \tan \theta$$

$$= \frac{\text{Rise}}{\text{Advance}}$$

Fig. 6-4

is a concept that focuses on the important aspect of the tangent, the reason we first got interested in tangents—namely, on the inclination or steepness of the curve. The slope of the tangent is tan θ, where θ is the angle between the tangent and the horizontal; it is, in other words, the ratio of the rise in height of the tangent to the corresponding horizontal increase. (Inclinations are generally expressed in terms of the slope; thus, for example, the inclination of an uphill stretch of highway or railroad is expressed in terms of so many feet of rise per so many feet forward. This is a more vivid means of expression than the actual *angle* of inclination, since most people do not have a very clear notion of how steep an angle of 30°—not to mention $\pi/6$ rad!— is, but everyone can picture how steep a slope of 1 ft of rise per 2 ft forward is.) In terms of the curve itself, the derivative (being the slope of the tangent) tells us how much the curve is rising per corresponding advance at the point P, i.e., what the ratio is between the infinitesimal rise and the infinitesimal horizontal advance to get from P to an infinitesimally close point O.[2]

As it stands, the definition of the derivative does not make it possible for us to find tangents with much ease under general conditions. To be sure, the geometrical definition we have given does enable us to solve the problem for certain special curves, albeit with much effort. As in the case of the definite integral, here too the major calculational advance came when the geometrical definitions were translated into algebraic terms; and we shall now proceed to this step.

[2] The dimensions of a derivative (see Chapter 2, Section 9) are the dimensions of a quotient, namely, "so many numerator units per single denominator unit." The latter half, "per *single* denominator unit," appears puzzling at first sight and deserves comment. Suppose we travel 100 mi in 2 hr, at steady speed. We find the speed by dividing the total change in distance by the total change in time $(100/2 = 50)$, arriving at a result which gives the speed in units of *mi per (single) hr.* Similarly, if we buy $\frac{1}{4}$ lb of butter for 10 cents, division of total price by the total weight $[10/(\frac{1}{4}) = 40]$ gives the price rate in *cents per (single) lb.* These examples illustrate how, in general, whether the quantity in the denominator *actually* changes by one, more than one, or less than one unit, the ratio is always expressed as "units of change in the numerator per *one* unit of change in the denominator." The sceptical reader should construct his own examples until he is satisfied that this is the case.

2. THE PROBLEM OF TANGENTS. THE ALGEBRAIC DEFINITION OF THE DERIVATIVE

Suppose our curve is described by the equation $y = f(x)$ in the xy-plane.[3] Our problem is to find the tangent to the curve at some point on the curve having, say, coordinates (x_1, y_1). [Remember that x_1 and y_1 are related by the functional relationship $y_1 = f(x_1)$, since the point (x_1, y_1) lies on the curve.] Now, "finding the tangent" means, in this way of looking at things, finding the equation of the straight line tangent to the curve at (x_1, y_1). To determine this equation we need only determine the *slope* of the tangent, since (see our discussion in Chapter 3, Section 4) the equation of a line is determined completely by the slope and by one point lying on the line [in this case (x_1, y_1)]. Thus, as in the previous section, our attention is focused on the *slope* of the tangent, or the *derivative*.

We shall now follow the prescription outlined in Section 1 for finding the derivative. First, draw a secant through P and a neighboring point O having coordinates $(x_1 + \Delta x, \ y_1 + \Delta y)$, where Δy and Δx are, respectively, the rise in height and the corresponding horizontal advance in going from P to O on the curve (Fig. 6-5). Since O is on the curve, its coordinates are also related by the functional relationship $y_1 + \Delta y = f(x_1 + \Delta x)$. The slope of the secant is given by

$$\text{secant slope} \equiv \frac{\Delta y}{\Delta x} = \frac{f(x_1 + \Delta x) - f(x_1)}{\Delta x} \qquad (6\text{-}1)$$

To obtain the slope of the tangent, we pass to the limit in which $O \to P$, i.e., O and P become separated by an infinitesimal dis-

---

[3] We shall restrict ourselves to planar curves, since these are the only ones we shall meet in practice. The algebraic discussion can be extended without difficulty to nonplanar curves, but the added complication is not necessary for us.

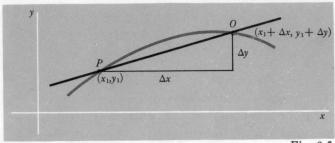

Fig. 6-5

tance *ds*. (As we noted, the limit is denoted by $\Delta s \to 0$ or, alternatively, by $\Delta x \to 0$, which amounts to the same thing.) In this limit, Δy and Δx become infinitesimal quantities (denoted by *dy* and *dx*, respectively) whose ratio is the slope of the tangent; the infinitesimal interval *ds* is no longer curved but is straight, as it must be inasmuch as it lies on the tangent. (We might note that in everyday experience any curved line—or surface— appears straight—or planar—if a small enough segment is looked at. For example, the immediate vicinity of the curved earth looks flat to us, at least when we observe it from earth-bound vantage points; and this was precisely why it was very natural and reasonable for many early scientists to hold that the earth is flat. Similarly, a basketball doubtless looks locally flat to an ant sitting on it.) Taking the liberty of exhibiting infinitesimals in a finite-sized drawing, we can picture the situation to be something like Fig. 6-6 (where the "*d*" notation reminds us that actually we are dealing with infinitesimals): The slope of the tangent is given

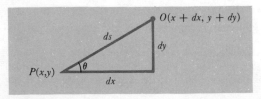

Fig. 6-6

by

$$\tan \theta = \text{slope of tangent} \equiv \text{derivative} \equiv \frac{dy}{dx} = \lim_{\Delta x \to 0} \frac{\Delta y}{\Delta x}$$

$$= \lim_{\Delta x \to 0} \frac{f(x_1 + \Delta x) - f(x_1)}{\Delta x} \qquad (6\text{-}2)$$

An alternative notation for the derivative, frequently used, is

$$f'(x) \equiv \frac{dy}{dx} \qquad (6\text{-}3)$$

It is common to call dy/dx, or $f'(x)$, "the derivative of y at x_1" (or "the derivative of the function f at x_1"). This is a shortened version of the more appropriate, but cumbersome, "the derivative at the point (x_1, y_1) of the curve $y = f(x)$." The process of finding the derivative is called "differentiation of the function $f(x)$," and one says that he is going "to differentiate the function $f(x)$" when he is setting out to find the derivative.

In terms of Eqs. 6-2 or 6-3, we can write the equation of the tangent to the curve at point P (see Chapter 3, Section 4):

$$\left.\begin{aligned} y - y_1 &= \left(\frac{dy}{dx}\right)_{\text{at } P} \cdot (x - x_1) \\ y - y_1 &= f'(x)_{\text{at } P} \cdot (x - x_1) \end{aligned}\right\} \qquad (6\text{-}4)$$

This completes the algebraic definition of the derivative in terms of which, as we shall now see, it becomes relatively simple to calculate the derivatives of many common functions.

3. EXAMPLES OF DERIVATIVES

We begin, as before, with examples for which the answer is known to us at the outset. Consider a curve which is simply a horizontal straight line, parallel to the x-axis a distance c above it (Fig. 6-7). The equation of this curve is $y = c$, and its slope

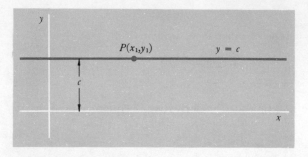

Fig. 6-7

(which does not vary from point to point, inasmuch as the curve is a straight line) is clearly 0, since the line is horizontal. Let us now go through the prescribed algebraic procedure for calculating the slope of the tangent to this curve at point (x_1,y_1)—a slope which will be the slope of the line itself, since a straight line is tangent to itself all along its length.

We consider the two neighboring points (x_1,y_1) and $(x_1 + \Delta x, y_1 + \Delta y)$, both lying on the curve. Since they lie on the curve, they must both satisfy the equation of the curve, $y = c$. This means that we must have $y_1 = c$ and $y_1 + \Delta y = c$, or $\Delta y = 0$. (All this is in effect quite obvious, since it merely states what we know—that there is no change in the height of the curve from point to point.) Therefore, for $y = c$, $\Delta y = 0$; and the quotient $\Delta y/\Delta x$ also must vanish for all neighboring points, since the numerator vanishes. This gives

$$\text{slope of tangent} \equiv \frac{dy}{dx} = \lim_{\Delta x \to 0} \frac{\Delta y}{\Delta x} = 0$$

for $y = c$; or

$$\frac{dc}{dx} = 0 \tag{6-5}$$

an answer in complete agreement with what we knew to be the case to begin with. Note that the answer is independent of the coordinates of the point P (neither x_1 nor y_1 appear in the answer) as should be the case for a straight line.

Let us carry out the differentiation of the more general linear function $y = mx + b$, which describes a straight line inclined to the x-axis, with slope m; Fig. 6-8 shows the graph of this function. We consider point P, with coordinates (x_1, y_1), and a neighboring

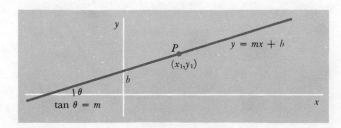

Fig. 6-8

point with coordinates $(x_1 + \Delta x, y_1 + \Delta y)$. Both points lie on the curve, so we have

$$y_1 = mx_1 + b \tag{6-6}$$

$$(y_1 + \Delta y) = m(x_1 + \Delta x) + b = mx_1 + m\,\Delta x + b \tag{6-7}$$

Subtracting Eq. 6-6 from Eq. 6-7, we find

$$\Delta y = m\,\Delta x \tag{6-8}$$

Thus we have

$$\frac{dy}{dx} = \lim_{\Delta x \to 0} \frac{\Delta y}{\Delta x} = \lim_{\Delta x \to 0} m = m$$

for $y = mx + b$; or

$$\frac{d}{dx}(mx + b) = m \tag{6-9}$$

Again we obtain the anticipated answer, and again it is independent of the coordinates of P, as it should be for a straight line.

We are now ready to proceed to a nonlinear case, where we do not know the answer in advance. Suppose we wish to find the slope of the tangent to the curve $y = x^2$ at the point P (see Fig. 6-9). Point P, with coordinates (x_1, y_1), and its neighboring point,

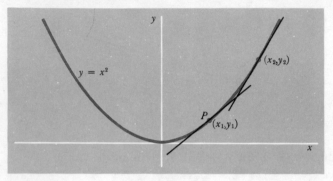

Fig. 6-9

with coordinates $(x_1 + \Delta x, y_1 + \Delta y)$, both lie on the curve and hence satisfy the equations:

$$y_1 = x_1^2 \qquad (6\text{-}10)$$

$$y_1 + \Delta y = (x_1 + \Delta x)^2 = x_1^2 + 2x_1 \Delta x + (\Delta x)^2 \qquad (6\text{-}11)$$

Subtracting Eq. 6-10 from Eq. 6-11, we find that

$$\Delta y = 2x_1 \Delta x + (\Delta x)^2$$

and hence the quotient we are interested in is

$$\frac{\Delta y}{\Delta x} = 2x_1 + \Delta x \qquad (6\text{-}12)$$

To find the derivative we are after, we must pass to the limit $\Delta x \to 0$ in Eq. 6-12. Now, in passing to the limit, $2x_1$ remains unaffected, but the term added to it, Δx, becomes vanishingly small; it is clear that when we pass to the limit $\Delta x \to 0$, all that is left on the right-hand side of Eq. 6-12 is $2x_1$. We note immediately that the result *does* depend on the coordinates of *P*, as we expected, since the slope of the tangent changes from point to point. To make clear precisely what we are doing, we shall introduce a new notation that shows explicitly *where* the derivative is being calculated:

$$\left(\frac{dy}{dx}\right)_{(x_1,y_1)} \equiv \frac{dy}{dx} \text{ [evaluated at } (x_1,y_1)] \tag{6-13}$$

Using this notation, we can summarize our results in the formula

$$\left(\frac{dy}{dx}\right)_{(x_1,y_1)} = \lim_{\Delta x \to 0} \left(\frac{\Delta y}{\Delta x}\right)_{(x_1,y_1)} = \lim_{\Delta x \to 0} (2x_1 + \Delta x) = 2x_1$$

for $y = x^2$; or

$$\left[\frac{d}{dx} (x^2)\right]_{(x_1,y_1)} = 2x_1 \tag{6-14}$$

Note: $\frac{d}{dx} (x^2)$ is another way of writing $\frac{d(x)^2}{dx}$ and, in general,

$\frac{d}{dx} f(x)$ is another way of writing $\frac{df(x)}{dx}$.

Carrying out the differentiation at some other point on the curve, having coordinates (x_2, y_2), yields

$$\left(\frac{dy}{dx}\right)_{(x_2,y_2)} = 2x_2 \tag{6-15}$$

and indeed for any arbitrary point on the curve, having coordinates (x, y), we obtain

$$\frac{dy}{dx} = 2x$$

for $y = x^2$; or

$$\frac{d}{dx} (x^2) = 2x \tag{6-16}$$

(where we have left out the parentheses and subscript attached to

dy/dx to indicate that the result as stated is valid for any point on the curve).

Proceeding now to the next power of x, we can find the derivative of $y = x^3$ (see Fig. 6-10). The coordinates of P and

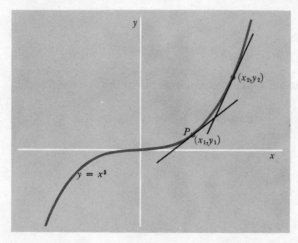

Fig. 6-10

its neighboring point, together with the relation they satisfy, are:

$$(x_1, y_1): \qquad y_1 = x_1^3 \qquad\qquad (6\text{-}17)$$

$$(x_1 + \Delta x, y_1 + \Delta y): y_1 + \Delta y = (x_1 + \Delta x)^3$$
$$= x_1^3 + 3x_1^2 \Delta x + 3x_1 \Delta x^2 + \Delta x^3 \quad (6\text{-}18)$$

Subtracting Eq. 6-17 from Eq. 6-18, we find

$$\Delta y = 3x_1^2 \Delta x + 3x_1 \Delta x^2 + \Delta x^3$$
$$\frac{\Delta y}{\Delta x} = 3x_1^2 + 3x_1 \Delta x + \Delta x^2 \qquad\qquad (6\text{-}19)$$

The two terms containing Δx on the right-hand side of Eq. 6-19 decrease in magnitude as Δx decreases, and become smaller and smaller relative to the leading term, $3x_1^2$. In the limit $\Delta x \to 0$, we find

$$\left(\frac{dy}{dx}\right)_{(x_1, y_1)} = \lim_{\Delta x \to 0} \left(\frac{\Delta y}{\Delta x}\right)_{(x_1, y_1)}$$
$$= \lim_{\Delta x \to 0} (3x_1^2 + 3x_1 \Delta x + \Delta x^2) = 3x_1^2$$

for $y = x^3$; or

$$\left[\frac{d}{dx} (x^3) \right]_{(x_1, y_1)} = 3x_1^2 \qquad (6\text{-}20)$$

Again we see that the answer depends on the coordinates of P, as it should, since the slope of the tangent obviously changes from point to point on the curve. If we had chosen to look at some other point having coordinates (x_2, y_2), we would have gotten the same answer as Eq. 6-20, with x_2 replacing x_1; and, in general, for an arbitrary point on the curve, having coordinates (x, y), we find

$$\frac{dy}{dx} = 3x^2 \qquad \text{for } y = x^3 \qquad (6\text{-}21)$$

Equations 6-16 and 6-21 give the derivatives of two powers of x, namely, x^2 and x^3. We have also found the derivatives of two other powers. Equation 6-5 holds for all constants c, in particular for $c = 1 = x^0$; and Eq. 6-9 holds for all values of m and b, in particular for $m = 1$, $b = 0$. Using these special values, we can write the following table for the derivatives of the first four nonnegative integral powers of x:

$$y = x^0: \qquad \frac{dy}{dx} = \frac{d}{dx} (x^0) = 0 \qquad (6\text{-}22)$$

$$y = x^1: \qquad \frac{dy}{dx} = \frac{d}{dx} (x^1) = 1 \quad (= 1 \cdot x^0)$$

$$y = x^2: \qquad \frac{dy}{dx} = \frac{d}{dx} (x^2) = 2x \qquad (6\text{-}23)$$

$$y = x^3: \qquad \frac{dy}{dx} = \frac{d}{dx} (x^3) = 3x^2$$

We might guess by examining this table that the derivative of the next power of x is:

$$y = x^4: \qquad \frac{dy}{dx} = \frac{d}{dx} (x^4) = 4x^3 \qquad (6\text{-}24)$$

And so it is. In standard calculus textbooks it is proved that, in general, for *all* real powers of x, positive, negative, or zero, integral, rational, or irrational, the following differentiation formula holds:

$$y = x^k: \qquad \frac{dy}{dx} = \frac{d}{dx}(x^k) = kx^{k-1} \qquad \text{for } k \text{ real} \qquad (6\text{-}25)$$

As would be expected, the derivative depends on the coordinates of the point at which it is being evaluated in all cases except for $k = 0$ and $k = 1$ (discussed earlier), since for all curves other than (horizontal or inclined) straight lines, the slope of the tangent changes from point to point on the curve.

4. SOME RULES OF DIFFERENTIATION

Suppose we know the derivative of a function $y = f(x)$ and we seek the derivative of a second function Y whose y-values for a given x are always c times the y-values of the first function— i.e., $Y = cy = cf(x)$. In finding the derivative of the second function we follow the same procedure, namely, find $Y_1 = cf(x_1)$, $Y_1 + \Delta Y = cf(x_1 + \Delta x)$, and subtract:

$$\Delta Y = cf(x_1 + \Delta x) - cf(x_1) = c[f(x_1 + \Delta x) - f(x_1)] \tag{6-26}$$

It is clear from Eq. 6-26 that the only difference between ΔY and Δy is a factor of c, as might be expected from the defined relationship between Y and y. This factor appears in the numerator of $\Delta y/\Delta x$ and, being a constant, is unaffected by passage to the limit dy/dx, so that we arrive at our first rule of differentiation:

$$\frac{d}{dx}(cy) = \frac{d}{dx}cf(x) = c\frac{dy}{dx} = cf'(x) \tag{6-27}$$

Suppose, now, that we have two functions, $u = f(x)$ and $v = g(x)$,

and we wish to find the derivative of their sum or difference—
that is, we wish to find the derivative of the function $y = h(x)$
defined by

$$y = u \pm v; \qquad h(x) = f(x) \pm g(x) \tag{6-28}$$

Applying the usual procedure, we find $y_1 = h(x_1)[= f(x_1) \pm g(x_1)]$, $y_1 + \Delta y = h(x_1 + \Delta x)[= f(x_1 + \Delta x) \pm g(x_1 + \Delta x)]$, and

$$\begin{aligned}
\Delta y &= h(x_1 + \Delta x) - h(x_1) \\
&= [f(x_1 + \Delta x) - f(x)] \pm [g(x_1 + \Delta x) - g(x)] \\
&= \Delta u \pm \Delta v \tag{6-29}
\end{aligned}$$

We see, then, that the numerator of the ratio that determines
the slope of y is the sum or difference of the numerators that
determine the slopes of u and v, respectively. Dividing by Δx and
passing to the limit, we find that

$$\left.\begin{aligned}
\frac{dy}{dx} &= \frac{du}{dx} \pm \frac{dv}{dx} & \text{for } y = u \pm v \\
h'(x) &= f'(x) \pm g'(x) & \text{for } h(x) = f(x) \pm g(x)
\end{aligned}\right\} \tag{6-30}$$

In other words, the derivative of a sum (or difference) is the sum
(or difference) of the derivatives of the separate terms.

Combining Eqs. 6-30 and 6-27, we can find the derivatives
of all sorts of functions, using only Eq. 6-25. For example, suppose
we want the derivative of

$$y = 5x^6 - x^2 + 4x \tag{6-31}$$

Applying Eq. 6-30, we find

$$\frac{dy}{dx} = \frac{d}{dx}(5x^6) - \frac{d}{dx}(x^2) + \frac{d}{dx}(4x)$$

and applying Eq. 6-27, this further simplifies to

$$\frac{dy}{dx} = 5\frac{d}{dx}(x^6) - \frac{d}{dx}(x^2) + 4\frac{dx}{dx}$$

which, with the aid of Eq. 6-25, gives the final answer:

$$\frac{dy}{dx} = 5(6x^5) - 2x + 4 = 30x^5 - 2x + 4 \qquad (6\text{-}32)$$

Sometimes we wish to find the derivative of a function which is the *product* of two other functions; for example, the function:

$$y = h(x) = uv = f(x)g(x) \qquad (6\text{-}33)$$

Proceeding in the usual fashion, we form $y_1 = u_1v_1$, $y_1 + \Delta y = (u_1 + \Delta u)(v_1 + \Delta v)$ and subtract:

$$\Delta y = (u_1 + \Delta u)(v_1 + \Delta v) - u_1v_1 = u_1 \, \Delta v + v_1 \, \Delta u + \Delta u \, \Delta v$$

Thus, the quotient is

$$\frac{\Delta y}{\Delta x} = u_1 \frac{\Delta v}{\Delta x} + v_1 \frac{\Delta u}{\Delta x} + \frac{\Delta u \, \Delta v}{\Delta x} \qquad (6\text{-}34)$$

Passing to the limit $\Delta x \to 0$, we find that the first two expressions on the right-hand side become $u_1(dv/dx)$ and $v_1(du/dx)$, respectively. The third expression becomes the product of a derivative, which is a finite quantity, multiplied by an infinitesimal [i.e., either $(du/dx) \cdot dv$ or $(dv/dx) \cdot du$, depending on how one wishes to group terms; the final result is unaffected by changing the grouping]; so that the product as a whole is infinitesimally small and negligible by comparison to the two finite quantities $u(dv/dx)$ and $v(du/dx)$ to which it is added. Thus, in the limit $\Delta x \to 0$, we obtain the following differentiation formula for products:

$$\left.\begin{aligned} \frac{dy}{dx} &= u \frac{dv}{dx} + v \frac{du}{dx} \qquad \text{for } y = uv \\ h'(x) &= f(x)g'(x) + f'(x)g(x) \\ &\qquad\qquad \text{for } h(x) = f(x)g(x) \end{aligned}\right\} \qquad (6\text{-}35)$$

If the product has more than two terms, the same type of rule applies, as can be seen by applying Eq. 6-35 twice in succession, first to $y = (uv)(w)$, then to the factor (uv):

$$\frac{dy}{dx} = uv\frac{dw}{dx} + u\frac{dv}{dx}w + \frac{du}{dx}vw \qquad \text{for } y = uvw \qquad (6\text{-}36)$$

In other words, to find the derivative of a product, one forms the sum of terms in which, successively, each factor is individually differentiated, the other factors remaining unchanged. The fact that the derivative of a product is *not* the product of the derivatives strikes us, perhaps, as surprising—about as surprising, say, as the fact that $(a + b)^n$ is not $a^n + b^n$!

If we wish to find the derivative of a quotient of functions, $y = u/v$, the following rule can be used:

$$\frac{dy}{dx} = \frac{v(du/dx) - u(dv/dx)}{v^2} \qquad \text{for } y = u/v \qquad (6\text{-}37)$$

The proof is left as an exercise.

Although Eq. 6-37 and especially Eqs. 6-35 and 6-36 find widespread use, it is a bit difficult for us to give examples of the application of these rules, since we have as yet a very limited repertory of functions to choose from—essentially, only powers of x; and, since the products and quotients of powers of x are again powers of x, we can apply Eq. 6-25 to them directly, without recourse to formulas for products and quotients. Nevertheless, for the sake of illustration, we shall calculate the derivative of $y = x^5$ (which we know by Eq. 6-25 to be $dy/dx = 5x^4$) by considering it to be the product of x^3 and x^2:

$$\frac{dy}{dx} = \frac{d}{dx}(x^3)(x^2) = x^3\frac{dx^2}{dx} + \frac{dx^3}{dx}(x^2) = x^3(2x) + (3x^2)(x^2)$$
$$= 2x^4 + 3x^4 = 5x^4 \qquad (6\text{-}38)$$

More complicated cases are treated in the same fashion, and we shall now extend our knowledge to include functions other than polynomials.

5. THE DERIVATIVE OF THE LOGARITHM.
NATURAL LOGARITHMS

Suppose we wish to find the slope of the tangent at point P to the logarithmic curve shown in Chapter 3, Fig. 3-15. Proceeding as prescribed, we write

$$y_1 = \log_{10} x_1 \qquad (6\text{-}39)$$
$$y_1 + \Delta y = \log_{10} (x_1 + \Delta x) \qquad (6\text{-}40)$$

Subtracting Eq. 6-39 from Eq. 6-40, we obtain

$$\Delta y = \log_{10} (x_1 + \Delta x) - \log_{10} x_1$$
$$= \log_{10} \left\{ \frac{x_1 + \Delta x}{x_1} \right\} = \log_{10} \left(1 + \frac{\Delta x}{x_1} \right) \quad (6\text{-}41)$$

Forming the quotient that gives the slope of the secant, we find

$$\frac{\Delta y}{\Delta x} = \frac{1}{\Delta x} \log_{10} \left\{ 1 + \frac{\Delta x}{x_1} \right\} \qquad (6\text{-}42)$$

Now, at first glance, the right-hand side of Eq. 6-42 appears quite obscure and mysterious, and it is not at all clear what will happen to it as we pass to the limit $\Delta x \to 0$. A second look reveals something piquant: as Δx becomes smaller, the expression in the bracket approaches 1, and its logarithm (to any base) approaches 0. Thus the right-hand side turns out to consist of two terms: (1) a numerator, a logarithm that approaches 0 as Δx does, and (2) a denominator which is Δx itself—so that the right-hand side appears to approach a quite indeterminate ratio as $\Delta x \to 0$.

Upon closer examination, the result turns out to be well determined after all. The entity that concerns us, the one in the brackets in Eq. 6-42, is seen not to involve the variable Δx alone, but the quotient $\Delta x / x_1 \equiv t$, which also approaches 0 as Δx does (since x_1 remains unaffected by passage to the limit). Introducing the variable t on the right side, using Eq. 2-19, and recalling that $\Delta x = x_1 t$, we can rewrite Eq. 6-42 as:

$$\frac{\Delta y}{\Delta x} = \frac{1}{x_1 t} \log_{10} (1 + t)$$

$$= \frac{1}{x_1} \cdot \frac{1}{t} \log_{10} (1 + t) = \frac{1}{x_1} \log_{10} (1 + t)^{1/t} \qquad (6\text{-}43)$$

Passing to the limit, we have

$$\left(\frac{dy}{dx}\right)_{(x_1, y_1)} = \lim_{\Delta x \to 0} \left(\frac{\Delta y}{\Delta x}\right)_{(x_1, y_1)} = \lim_{t \to 0} \frac{1}{x_1} \log_{10} (1 + t)^{1/t}$$

$$= \frac{1}{x_1} \lim_{t \to 0} \log_{10} (1 + t)^{1/t} \qquad \text{for } y = \log_{10} x$$

$$(6\text{-}44)$$

The entire problem of differentiating the logarithm is seen to revolve about the problem of evaluating the limit:

$$\lim_{t \to 0} \log_{10} (1 + t)^{1/t} \qquad (6\text{-}45)$$

or, more directly, the limit:

$$\lim_{t \to 0} (1 + t)^{1/t} \qquad (6\text{-}46)$$

since the limit in Eq. 6-45 is just the logarithm to the base 10 of the limit in Eq. 6-46. As we have already noted, the limit involves two "tendencies"—the tendency of the expression in parentheses to 1, and the tendency of the exponent to infinity ($1/t \to \infty$ as $t \to 0$). The "balance" between these tendencies is critical: If the expression in the bracket were exactly *equal* to 1, then the expression raised to *any* power, no matter how large, would be equal to 1; if the expression in the bracket remained permanently greater than 1 by a *finite* amount (however small), then the expression raised to an endlessly increasing power would itself increase without bound. In no other example that we will treat does the delicate and intricate nature of the limiting process reveal itself so clearly.

Let us calculate some values of $(1 + t)^{1/t}$ for a few decreasing values of t, to get an idea of the order of magnitude of the limiting value of Eq. 6-46:

t	1	$\frac{1}{2}$	$\frac{1}{3}$	$\frac{1}{4}$	$\frac{1}{10}$	$\frac{1}{20}$	$\frac{1}{100}$	$\frac{1}{1,000}$	$\frac{1}{10,000}$
$(1 + t)^{1/t}$	2	2.25	2.370	2.441	2.594	2.653	2.704	2.7171	2.7182

The limit can be evaluated to any desired accuracy, as is shown in the standard texts. To four decimal places, it turns out to be 2.7183. The number defined by limit is commonly designated by the letter e.[4] Thus we have:

$$e \equiv \lim_{t \to 0} (1 + t)^{1/t} = 2.718 \text{ (to three decimal places)}$$

$$(6\text{-}47)$$

In terms of this number, the derivative we were looking for in Eq. 6-44 becomes:

$$\left(\frac{dy}{dx}\right)_{(x_1, y_1)} = \frac{1}{x_1} \log_{10} e \qquad \text{for } y = \log_{10} x$$

and for an arbitrary point on the logarithm curve, and an arbitrary base a, we obtain:

$$\frac{dy}{dx} = \frac{d}{dx} (\log_a x) = \frac{1}{x} \log_a e \qquad \text{for } y = \log_a x \qquad (6\text{-}48)$$

The right-hand side of our final result, Eq. 6-48, is the product of two factors: one depends on the coordinates and one depends on the choice of base for logarithms. The latter just

---

[4] A special symbol is needed for the number because it is used frequently and cannot be expressed as a finite decimal, as a fraction, or as a root. A similar situation holds for the number π, the ratio of the circumference of a circle to its diameter. π to three decimals is 3.142; but the symbol π stands for the exact number defined geometrically in the preceding sentence. Both e and π have played important roles in modern mathematics, each being an example of transcendental numbers—of which there is an infinity of potential examples, although only rarely can specific numbers be *proved* to be transcendental. See the extremely readable book by A. A. Fränkel, *Abstract Set Theory* (1st ed., Amsterdam: North-Holland, 1953), especially pp. 74–75.

sits there reminding us of our follies, for if we had only chosen our base wisely, it would not have been there at all. Specifically, if we had taken our *base* to be *the number e*, the second factor would be $\log_e e = 1$!

This suggests that we switch once and for all to the base e, and calculate all logarithms to that base. Logarithms to the base e are given the name "natural logarithms," since their use is in a sense pointed to by the very nature of calculus, while logarithms to the base 10 are called "common logarithms," in accordance with their widespread use. In the absence of a table of natural logarithms, the logarithm to the base e can always be calculated from the logarithm to the base 10, using the "change of base" formula derived in Chapter 2, Eq. 2-24, together with the fact that

$$\log_e 10 = 2.303 \quad \text{(to three decimal places)} \quad (6\text{-}49)$$

Hereafter, whenever we use the symbol "log" without designating the base, the base e will be understood.

In conclusion, we can now write in place of Eq. 6-48, for all our future use,

$$\frac{dy}{dx} = \frac{d}{dx}(\log x) = \frac{1}{x} \quad \text{for } y = \log x \quad (6\text{-}50)$$

—a particularly simple and elegant result, worthy of all the labor we put in to find it!

6. INVERSE FUNCTIONS. THE DERIVATIVE OF THE EXPONENTIAL

A functional relationship between y and x relates pairs of values of the variable. If the relation is one-to-one—that is, if one and only one value of x is paired with one and only one value of y—then it makes no difference which variable we treat as dependent and which as independent: Regardless of how we look at it, each variable determines the other uniquely. In such cases, if the relation between x and y is described by the functional relationship $y = f(x)$, we can just as easily invert this and find a functional relationship $x = \phi(y)$. The functions f and ϕ are called "inverse functions."

When the pairing is not biunique (one-to-one), care must be exercised, and the inversion cannot be performed without some special additional stipulations.

Examples are easy to find. Thus, the relation $y = mx + b$ ($m \neq 0$) can be inverted to $x = (1/m)(y - b)$; the relation $y = x^3$ can be inverted to $x = \sqrt[3]{y} = y^{\frac{1}{3}}$; and the relation $y = \log x$ can be inverted to $x = e^y$. On the other hand, a function such as $y = x^2$ is *not* biunique, since two values of x having the same magnitude and opposite signs correspond to the same value of y. This ambiguity makes simple inversion impossible, as we learn when we are taught that $y = x^2$ implies $x = \pm \sqrt{y}$. An inversion can be carried out if we agree to restrict ourselves, say, to the positive sign alone.

The derivatives of inverse functions have the following simple property: they are the inverses of each other. This can be seen most simply algebraically: in finding the derivative of $y = f(x)$, we form the quotient $\Delta y / \Delta x = [f(x + \Delta x) - f(x)]/\Delta x$, while in finding the derivative of $x = \phi(y)$, we form the quotient $\Delta x / \Delta y = [\phi(y + \Delta y) - \phi(y)]/\Delta y$. The quotients $\Delta y / \Delta x$ and $\Delta x / \Delta y$ are inverses—$\Delta y / \Delta x = 1/(\Delta x / \Delta y)$—for *all* finite values of Δy and Δx, and remain inverses in the limit. Thus we have:

$$
\begin{aligned}
dy/dx &= 1/(dx/dy) \\
f'(x) &= 1/\phi'(y)
\end{aligned}
\quad
\begin{aligned}
&\text{for } y = f(x) \text{ and its} \\
&\text{inverse } x = \phi(y)
\end{aligned}
\qquad (6\text{-}51)
$$

This can also be pictured graphically. The derivative dy/dx is $\tan \theta$, where θ is the angle between the tangent to the curve and the x-axis; the derivative dx/dy is $\tan \psi$, where ψ is the angle between the tangent and the y-axis (see Fig. 6-11). Since θ and

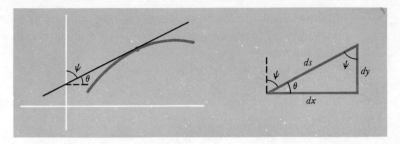

Fig. 6-11

ψ are complementary angles, we have

$$\sin \theta = \cos \psi, \cos \theta = \sin \psi \rightarrow$$
$$\tan \theta = \sin \theta/\cos \theta = \cos \psi/\sin \psi = 1/\tan \psi$$

$$(6\text{-}52)$$

which is just Eq. 6-51 all over again.

With the aid of Eq. 6-51 we can find derivatives of new functions that are inverses of functions whose derivatives we know, without going through the limiting process in each case. Let us find the derivatives for each of the three inverse functions we used as examples earlier. Suppose we start with

$$s = mt + b \qquad\qquad (6\text{-}53)$$

where we use s and t to designate variables. Then we know that

$$\frac{ds}{dt} = m \qquad\qquad (6\text{-}54)$$

The inverse of Eq. 6-53 is

$$t = (1/m)(s - b)$$
$$= (1/m)s - b/m \qquad\qquad (6\text{-}55)$$

By Eq. 6-51, we have

$$\frac{dt}{ds} = \frac{1}{(ds/dt)} = 1/m \qquad\qquad (6\text{-}56)$$

which we know to be correct, since it is easy to find dt/ds directly from Eq. 6-55, inasmuch as the inverse of a linear function is a linear function.

Now let us begin with

$$s = t^3 \tag{6-57}$$

whose derivative we know to be

$$\frac{ds}{dt} = 3t^2 \tag{6-58}$$

The inverse of Eq. 6-57 is

$$t = \sqrt[3]{s} = s^{\frac{1}{3}} \tag{6-59}$$

and by Eq. 6-51 we have

$$\frac{dt}{ds} = \frac{1}{(ds/dt)} = \frac{1}{3t^2} = \frac{1}{3\sqrt[3]{s^2}} = \frac{1}{3s^{\frac{2}{3}}} = (\tfrac{1}{3})s^{-\frac{2}{3}} \tag{6-60}$$

which, again, we could have found by direct application of Eq. 6-25 to Eq. 6-59.

We shall now use Eq. 6-51 to find a *new* differentiation formula. We begin with

$$s = \log t \tag{6-61}$$

whose derivative we have seen in Eq. 6-50 is

$$\frac{ds}{dt} = \frac{1}{t} \tag{6-62}$$

The inverse of Eq. 6-61 is

$$t = e^s \tag{6-63}$$

and, by Eq. 6-51,

$$\frac{dt}{ds} = \frac{1}{(ds/dt)} = \frac{1}{(1/t)} = t \tag{6-64}$$

Returning to our more accustomed variables, x and y, we can write Eqs. 6-63 and 6-64 as the following addition to our list of derivatives:

$$\frac{dy}{dx} = y$$

for $y = e^x$; or

$$\frac{d}{dx}(e^x) = e^x \tag{6-65}$$

In other words, the exponential is a function whose derivative is equal to itself; the slope of the tangent to the exponential curve at any point is equal in magnitude to the height of that point above the x-axis.

A slight modification of Eq. 6-65 is also of considerable use. Suppose we begin with the logarithm function multiplied by a constant:

$$u = c \log v \tag{6-66}$$

Then Eq. 6-50 and the differentiation rule Eq. 6-27 give:

$$\frac{du}{dv} = c\frac{d}{dv}(\log v) = \frac{c}{v} \tag{6-67}$$

The inverse of Eq. 6-66 is

$$v = e^{u/c} \tag{6-68}$$

and Eq. 6-51 tells us that

$$\frac{dv}{du} = \frac{1}{(du/dv)} = v/c \tag{6-69}$$

Returning to (x,y) variables, and using k instead of $1/c$, we can write:

$$\frac{dy}{dx} = ky$$

for $y = e^{kx}$; or

$$\frac{d}{dx}(e^{kx}) = ke^{kx} \tag{6-70}$$

7. THE DERIVATIVES OF TRIGONOMETRIC FUNCTIONS

To calculate the derivative of $y = \sin x$, we proceed as usual to write

$$y = \sin x \tag{6-71}$$
$$y + \Delta y = \sin (x + \Delta x) \tag{6-72}$$

and to subtract Eq. 6-71 from Eq. 6-72, obtaining the quotient

$$\frac{\Delta y}{\Delta x} = \frac{\sin (x + \Delta x) - \sin x}{\Delta x} \tag{6-73}$$

Using Eq. 4-10 for $\sin (a + b)$, we can rewrite Eq. 6-73 as:

$$\frac{\Delta y}{\Delta x} = \frac{\sin x \cos \Delta x}{\Delta x} + \frac{\cos x \sin \Delta x}{\Delta x} - \frac{\sin x}{\Delta x} \tag{6-74}$$

Before passing to the limit $\Delta x \to 0$, we must find out what happens to $\cos \Delta x$ and $\sin \Delta x$ as the angle Δx becomes small. Recalling that the measure of an angle in radians is the ratio of intercepted arc to radius, we shall investigate this question with the aid of

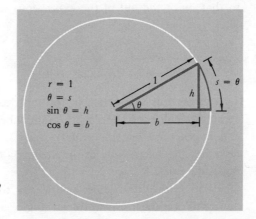

Fig. 6-12

a circle of *unit* radius, in which the size of angle is directly equal to the magnitude of the intercepted arc. Figure 6-12 shows such a unit circle, having the apex of an angle θ at its center and having the magnitudes relevant to calculation of the sine and cosine functions clearly marked. Use of a unit radius simplifies the expressions for the angle and its functions.

Now, for a *small* angle Δx, the relevant sector of the unit circle looks something like Fig. 6-13. We see that, for a small angle, the difference in magnitude between the height h and the arc segment Δs is small, as is also the difference between the base b and the radius 1. In the limit $\Delta x \rightarrow 0$, we have

$$\left.\begin{array}{l} h \rightarrow \Delta s = \Delta x \\ b \rightarrow \text{radius} = 1 \end{array}\right\} \qquad\qquad (6\text{-}75)$$

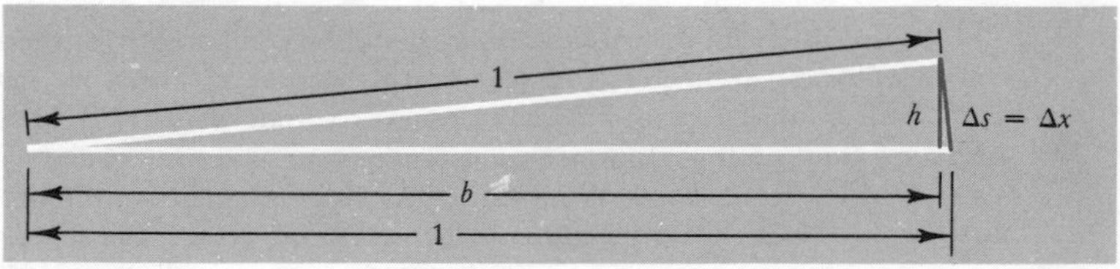

Fig. 6-13

so that, with the aid of the expressions written in Fig. 6-12, we have

$$\sin \Delta x \to \Delta x \qquad \text{as } \Delta x \to 0 \qquad \qquad (6\text{-}76)$$
$$\cos \Delta x \to 1 \qquad \text{as } \Delta x \to 0 \qquad \qquad (6\text{-}77)$$

To express this in words: In the limit as the angle approaches zero, the value of the cosine approaches unity (adjacent side and hypotenuse become equal), and the value of the sine approaches the magnitude of the angle (both approaching zero as the angle does).[5]

The entire discussion points up the convenience of the "natural" radian measure of an angle, as opposed to the arbitrary degree measure. Had we not been working with an angle measure for which $\theta = s$, all the limits would have been more complicated, and would have involved constants that depend on the choice of angle measure.

With the aid of Eqs. 6-76 and 6-77 we can pass to the limit $\Delta x \to 0$ in Eq. 6-74. Equation 6-77 tells us that the first term on the right-hand side of Eq. 6-74, $(\sin x) \cdot (\cos \Delta x)/\Delta x$, approaches $\sin x/\Delta x$ as $\Delta x \to 0$—i.e., becomes equal in magnitude to the third term on the right, so that in the limit the two terms cancel. Equation 6-76 tells us that the ratio $(\sin \Delta x)/\Delta x \to 1$ as $\Delta x \to 0$, so that the second term on the right $\to \cos x$. We can thus write the differentiation formula:

$$\frac{dy}{dx} = \cos x$$

---

[5] This statement concerning limits should be compared with the known values of cos 0, sin 0, found in Chapter 4, Section 5. There we saw that cos 0 = 1, so that Eq. 6-77 adds little new to what we already knew. We also saw that sin 0 = 0, which is in agreement with Eq. 6-76, since as $\Delta x \to 0$, sin $\Delta x \to \Delta x \to 0$. What Eq. 6-76 *adds* over and above the statement that sin 0 = 0 is the statement that for very small angles, the sine and the angle are almost equal in magnitude (sin $\theta \sim \theta$ for small θ), and this is a significant new fact.

for $y = \sin x$; or

$$\frac{d}{dx} (\sin x) = \cos x \qquad (6\text{-}78)$$

It is left as an exercise to prove the following formula, using Eq. 4-12 for cos $(a + b)$ and the limits in Eqs. 6-76 and 6-77:

$$\frac{dy}{dx} = -\sin x$$

for $y = \cos x$; or

$$\frac{d}{dx} (\cos x) = -\sin x \qquad (6\text{-}79)$$

8. THE SOLUTION OF THE PROBLEM OF TANGENTS. RELATED PROBLEMS

It should by now be unnecessary to belabor the point that the derivative, defined as the limit of a particular quotient, is by definition the slope of the tangent to the curve at point P. As in the case of the integral, here too we have no independent way of finding the entity we are after, so that the one way we are left with can only be considered a *definition* of that entity. Of course, the definition has been arrived at on the basis of our intuitive appreciation of the problem and has been found to give the expected answer in the few cases where an independent determination is known; but for the general case we can do no more than *define* the slope of the tangent to be the derivative.

The derivative has wide applications beyond the geometrical one of determining a tangent, although these applications are suggested by the geometrical one. The tangent to a curve, as we have seen, shows us how *steep* the curve is at the point in question—tells us at what rate it is rising (or falling), so many units up per so many units across. This suggests that whenever we wish to know the rate at which something is changing with respect to something—i.e., how many units it is increasing (or decreasing) per so many units change in the other thing—the derivative will provide us with the answer.

This suggestion is borne out by the algebraic definition of the derivative in terms of a functional relationship between two variables. The algebraic definition shows us that the derivative of a function, evaluated for a given pair of values of the variables, is nothing other than the *ratio of the amount one variable changes to the amount the other changes* over an infinitesimal interval; it is, in other words, *the rate of change of one variable with respect to the other variable* at the pair of values (the point) in question. The rate of change must be found by resorting to a limiting process because, with the exception of the case where the variables are related by a linear function, the rate of change differs for different pairs of values of the variable; hence, to find this rate of change for a given pair (x_1, y_1), we must restrict ourselves to the immediate infinitesimal range of values adjacent to that pair.

Thus, in general, if we have two variables related by some functional relationship, the derivative at a point tells us how much one variable is changing with respect to the other at that point. For example, if the variables are I, the net interest accruing on a sum of money lying in a bank, and t is the time elapsed, dI/dt will be the marginal rate of change, i.e., the rate at which the net interest is changing *with time*. If the variables are P, the net money paid out as interest by a bank, and T, the total value of all accounts of all types, dP/dT will be the rate of increase of the bank's outgoing interest payments *with respect to its total capital*.

The derivative thus emerges as a very important tool in the study of change, inasmuch as it tells us always the rate of change at any given point or instant. It is in this capacity that it finds its greatest use in the sciences.

EXERCISES

1. Differentiate with respect to x: $y = 2x^3 - x^2 + 6x - 5$; $y = -3 + 2x + 14x^2 + 17x^3 + 12x^4$; $y = 6x + 13x^3 - 7x^4$.

2. If $x = y^2 - 5y + 3$, what is dx/dy? If $t = 3s^2 + 4$, what is dt/ds?

3. If $Q = a + bT + cT^2 + dT^3$, what is dQ/dT?

4. Differentiate: $y = 1/x^{10}$; $y = 3/x^2 + 4/x - x + 1$; $y = (x - 1)/(x + 1)$; $y = (x^2 - x)(x^2 + 2)$; $u = 3y/(16 - y^2)$; $s = t^2/(t - 1)$; $y = x(x - 1)/(x^2 - 4)$; $y = 1/(a + bx)$; $y = mx^n - nx^m$; $y = (x^n - x^{-n})/x$.

5. Find the coordinates for which the slope of the tangent to $y = x^3 - 12x + 1$ is 0.

6. Prove Eq. 6-15 explicitly.

7. Prove Eq. 6-36.

8. Differentiate: $y = x \log x$; $y = (\log x)/x$; $y = (\log x)/x^2 - 1/x^2$.

9. Find the derivatives of: $r = \sin \theta \cos \theta$; $y = 10/(\cos x + 2 \sin x)$; $y = \cos x + \sin x$; $y = (1 + \sin x)/(1 - \sin x)$; $y = x^2 \sin x - 2 \sin x + 2x \cos x$; $y = 2x \sin x + 2 \cos x - x^2 \cos x$; $y = x \sin x + \cos x$; $y = (\sin x)/(1 - \cos x)$.

10. Find the derivatives with respect to x of the following secondary trigonometric functions: $\tan x$; $\cot x \equiv \cos x/\sin x$ (the cotangent function); $\sec x \equiv 1/\cos x$ (the secant function); $\operatorname{cosec} x \equiv 1/\sin x$ (the cosecant function).

11. Differentiate $y = (\sin x)/x$.

12. Differentiate: $y = e^{-cx}$; $y = xe^x$; $y = xe^{-x}$; $y = x^2 e^{-x}$; $y = e^{-x} \cos x$; $y = (e^x + e^{-x})/2$; $y = (e^x - e^{-x})/(e^x + e^{-x})$.

13. Using the formula for $d(\log_a x)/dx$, find da^x/dx.

14. What is the rate of change of the volume of a cube with respect to the length of an edge?

15. Show that the rate of change of the volume of a sphere with respect to the radius is equal to the surface area. (Try to understand this result pictorially.)

7

THE FUNDAMENTAL
THEOREM
OF CALCULUS

1. THE THEOREM. UNIFICATION OF CALCULUS

The key to the relationship between derivative and integral was the concept of *the rate of change of an area*, as its right-hand boundary is moved. Specifically, the crucial question turned out to be: What is the rate of change of the total area enclosed between the curve $y = f(x)$, the x-axis, and two lines perpendicular to the x-axis at a and at some point x, with respect to a change in the right-hand boundary (see Fig. 7-1)?

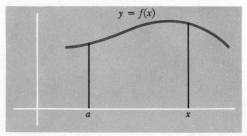

Fig. 7-1

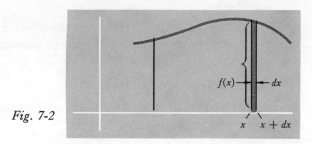

Fig. 7-2

The area so defined clearly depends on the position of the right boundary; for any particular choice of x, the area has a specific value, each choice of x corresponding to some uniquely determined area. The area A is thus a function of x, which we will designate by $A(x)$; by the definition of the definite integral, $A(x)$ is:

$$A(x) = \int_a^x f(x)\, dx \qquad (7\text{-}1)$$

In terms of Eq. 7-1, our question—What is the rate of change of $A(x)$ with respect to x?—can be written: What is $dA(x)/dx$?—

$$\frac{d}{dx} A(x) = \frac{d}{dx} \int_a^x f(x)\, dx = \frac{d}{dx} \int_a^x y\, dx = ? \qquad (7\text{-}2)$$

Let us recall, briefly and loosely, the definitions of the definite integral and the derivative. The *definite integral* is just the sum of all the rectangular strips into which the area is divided, each strip having (infinitesimal) width dx and height $y = f(x)$ —i.e., height equal to the height of the curve at the position of the strip. Thus, for example, in Fig. 7-1, if we were to continue the integral beyond the right boundary drawn at x, the next strip to the right would have width dx, and height $y = f(x)$—i.e., height equal to the value of y at the boundary; in other words, height equal to the height of the boundary (see Fig. 7-2). The *derivative* of the area with respect to x is just the ratio of the infinitesimal change in area (brought about by an infinitesimal change in the boundary x) to the infinitesimal change in x. From what we have said, and from the figure, we see that the magnitude of the infinitesimal increase in area corresponding to a shift in boundary from x to $x + dx$ is:

$$dA = f(x)\, dx = y\, dx \tag{7-3}$$

Dividing by the change in x—i.e., by dx—we find that the derivative in question is:

$$\frac{d}{dx}\, A(x) = \frac{d}{dx}\int_a^x f(x)\, dx = f(x)$$

$$= \frac{d}{dx}\int_a^x y\, dx = y \text{ (evaluated at the right-} \tag{7-4}$$
$$\text{hand boundary, } x)$$

Equation 7-4 is known as the Fundamental Theorem of Calculus. It states, in words, that the derivative of the definite integral of a function with respect to its upper limit is just the function evaluated at the upper limit; or, alternatively, that the rate of change of the area with respect to a shift of the right-hand boundary is the height of the boundary in question.

The importance of this theorem will become evident shortly. For our part, we can justly wonder at the insight that led Newton and Leibnitz to consider the problem symbolized by Eq. 7-2. To us, the fact that this is an interesting problem is far from obvious at first sight. To the fashioners of calculus, the realization that its solution would serve as the keystone in the archway connecting the realm of derivatives with that of integrals could hardly have been less than an exhilarating revelation.

2. ANTIDERIVATIVES

Equation 7-4 tells us that $A(x)$, the magnitude of the area under $y = f(x)$ bounded by a and x, is a function of x whose derivative is $f(x)$. In general, if we have a function $y = f(x)$, any other function (such as $A(x)$) whose derivative is $f(x)$ is called an *antiderivative* of x. To understand better the relationship between $A(x)$ and $f(x)$, between definite integrals and derivatives, we shall study first the nature of antiderivatives.

Whenever we write a differentiation formula, we are at the same time giving a pair of functions related as derivative and antiderivative. Consider the differentiation formula

$$\frac{d}{dx}(x^2) = 2x$$

This tells us that the derivative of x^2 is $2x$. It also tells us that if we start with the function $2x$ and seek another function whose derivative is $2x$, one such other function is x^2; or, in other words, it also tells us that an antiderivative of $f(x) = 2x$ is $F(x) = x^2$ (where we designate the antiderivatives by a capital letter, the original function by a small letter). Thus, a differentiation formula

$$\frac{d}{dx} F(x) = f(x) \tag{7-5}$$

can be viewed not only as giving the derivative of $F(x)$, but also as giving at the same time an antiderivative of $f(x)$.

Note that we have been careful to refer to *an* antiderivative of $f(x)$, rather than to *the* antiderivative of $f(x)$. This is because any given function $f(x)$ always has more than one antiderivative. For example, x^2 is not the only function whose derivative is $2x$; consider the function

$$y = x^2 + 5 \tag{7-6}$$

The derivative of this function is found with the aid of the rules of differentiation to be:

$$\frac{dy}{dx} = \frac{d}{dx}(x^2 + 5) = \frac{d}{dx}(x^2) + \frac{d}{dx}(5) = 2x + 0 = 2x \tag{7-7}$$

In fact, *any* function consisting of the sum of x^2 and a constant will have derivative $2x$, and thus be an antiderivative of $2x$, as we can see from Eq. 7-7. In general, because the derivative of a constant is 0, if we have *one* antiderivative of $f(x)$, say $F(x)$, then all functions $F(x) + c$ formed by adding a constant to $F(x)$ will also be antiderivatives of $f(x)$.

The problem now suggests itself, whether *all* the antiderivatives of a function $f(x)$ differ at most by an additive constant or whether they can differ in a more substantial way. The answer to this question can be found as follows. Suppose we start with a function $f(x)$ which has two different antiderivatives, $F(x)$ and $G(x)$. This means that

$$\frac{d}{dx} F(x) = f(x)$$
$$\frac{d}{dx} G(x) = f(x)$$

(7-8)

Let us examine the difference between these functions, $F(x) - G(x)$, which we shall denote by $H(x)$:

$$H(x) \equiv F(x) - G(x) \qquad (7\text{-}9)$$

Our question can then be rephrased to be: What is the nature of $H(x)$? In particular, is $H(x)$ always a constant (and thus, in fact, independent of x) or can it be something else?

One property of $H(x)$ that is known to us from Eqs. 7-8 and 7-9 is its derivative:

$$\frac{d}{dx} H(x) = \frac{d}{dx} F(x) - \frac{d}{dx} G(x) = f(x) - f(x) = 0 \quad (7\text{-}10)$$

We see that $H(x)$ is a function whose derivative is always 0—i.e., the graph $y = H(x)$ has slope 0 everywhere. We have seen already that this means the graph must be a horizontal straight line, so that $y = H(x) = c$. This completes the demonstration of the following important theorem: If $F(x)$ and $G(x)$ are any two antiderivatives of the same function $f(x)$, they can differ at most by a constant:

$$F(x) - G(x) = c \qquad (7\text{-}11)$$

Thus, in effect, all we even need to know is *one* antiderivative of a function, say, $F(x)$; all the others will differ from this one by additive constants, and we can provide alternative antiderivatives to our heart's content by adding different constants to $F(x)$.

3. THE DEFINITE INTEGRAL AND ANTIDERIVATIVES. THE INDEFINITE INTEGRAL

Let us return to the fundamental theorem and especially to Eq. 7-4, which states that the definite integral from a to some point x, i.e., the function $A(x)$, is an antiderivative of the integrand $f(x)$. From the definition of the particular function $A(x)$, given in Eq. 7-1, we see that

$$A(b) = \int_a^b f(x)\, dx \qquad (7\text{-}12)$$

Thus, $A(b)$ is the definite integral of $f(x)$ from a to b. Suppose, now, that we have an *arbitrary* antiderivative of $f(x)$ that we shall designate by $F(x)$:

$$\frac{d}{dx} F(x) = f(x) \qquad (7\text{-}13)$$

Then, since $F(x)$ and $A(x)$ are both antiderivatives of $f(x)$, the theorem 7-11 tells us that they differ at most by a constant:

$$A(x) = F(x) + c \qquad (7\text{-}14)$$

To evaluate the constant, we must evaluate Eq. 7-14 at some particular point x. A point for which Eq. 7-14 becomes particularly simple is $x = a$, since here $A(x) = 0$:

$$A(a) = \int_a^a f(x)\, dx = 0 \qquad (7\text{-}15)$$

because the upper and lower limit coincide, so that we are left simply with a line at $x = a$ having 0 area (see Fig. 7-3). Using

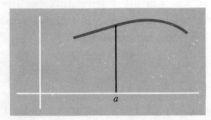

Fig. 7-3

Eq. 7-15, we find from Eq. 7-14 that

$$A(a) = 0 = F(a) + c \;\rightarrow\; c = -F(a) \qquad (7\text{-}16)$$

so that the constant is now known, and Eq. 7-14 can be rewritten

$$A(x) = F(x) - F(a) \qquad (7\text{-}17)$$

In particular, this tells us that the definite integral in Eq. 7-12 has the value

$$\int_a^b f(x)\, dx = F(b) - F(a) \equiv F(x)\,\Big|_a^b \qquad (7\text{-}18)$$

where we use the notation introduced in Chapter 5. Equation 7-18 tells us that *if we know any antiderivative $F(x)$ of $f(x)$, the definite integral of a function $f(x)$ from a to b can be evaluated, and has the value $F(b) - F(a)$*. This is where the fundamental theorem leads (with the aid of some insight!), and this is the result which binds integration and differentiation into one discipline. As far as integration is concerned, this result replaces the tedium of finding the limits of infinite sums by the far simpler task of finding antiderivatives from tables of functions and their derivatives. With the aid of Eq. 7-18, we can now construct a table of integrals as extensive as our table of derivatives.

Before doing this we shall introduce a common notation and usage which is based on the fundamental theorem and on Eq. 7-18. An (arbitrary) antiderivative of a function $f(x)$ is usually also called "an *indefinite* integral of $f(x)$" or even simply "an integral of $f(x)$"[6]; and is denoted, instead of by $F(x)$, by the symbol

$$\int f(x)\ dx \equiv F(x) \tag{7-19}$$

—in other words, by the integral symbol without the limits attached. One has, by definition,

$$\frac{d}{dx} \int f(x)\ dx = f(x) \tag{7-20}$$

which suggests to the eye what we know, that integration and differentiation are reciprocal procedures: The integral of a function is an antiderivative of the function, so that the derivative of the integral is the function itself. In this sense, taking the derivative "erases" the integral, i.e., "undoes" what integration does to a function. The symbol introduced in Eq. 7-19 also has the advantage that the value of the *definite* integral from a to b is denoted by the same symbol, simply adding subscript a and superscript b.

4. A TABLE OF INTEGRALS

Using our table of derivatives and our discussion around Eq. 7-5, we can construct a table of integrals. For example, consider the relation

$$\frac{d}{dx}(x^k) = kx^{k-1} \qquad (k\ \text{real}) \tag{7-21}$$

---

[6] Also to be found in the literature is the unfortunate nomenclature "*the* indefinite integral" or "*the* integral."

This tells us immediately that

$$\int kx^{k-1}\, dx = x^k \qquad (k \text{ real}) \tag{7-22}$$

(Note that all powers of x are covered by the expression of the left side of Eq. 7-22, except for $x^{-1} = 1/x$, since the k corresponding to x^{-1} is $k = 0$, for which the left side vanishes. Thus, it is not possible to find the integral of $1/x$—and only of $1/x$—with the aid of Eq. 7-21. Although this may seem odd, it will soon become perfectly clear.) Dividing by k (which can therefore not $= 0$) and using the rules of integration, we find:

$$\int x^{k-1}\, dx = (1/k)x^k \qquad (k \text{ real}, \neq 0) \tag{7-23}$$

As an integral formula, Eq. 7-23 is a bit clumsy, since one wants to see right away what the integral of x to some power is, not the integral of x to a power written "$k - 1$." For convenience, then, we introduce the symbol $m \equiv k - 1$ and obtain:

$$\int x^m\, dx = \left(\frac{1}{m+1}\right) x^{m+1} \qquad (m \neq -1) \tag{7-24}$$

This is our first integral formula, and it is seen, with the aid of Eqs. 7-19 and 7-18, to be the same as the integral formula derived in Chapter 5, Eq. 5-24.

For the logarithm and exponential, we have:

$$\frac{d}{dx}(e^x) = e^x \rightarrow \int e^x\, dx = e^x \tag{7-25}$$

$$\frac{d}{dx}(e^{kx}) = ke^{kx} \rightarrow \int e^{kx}\, dx = (1/k)e^{kx} \tag{7-26}$$

$$\frac{d}{dx}(\log x) = \frac{1}{x} \rightarrow \int \left(\frac{1}{x}\right) dx = \int x^{-1}\, dx = \log x \tag{7-27}$$

Equation (7-27) shows us what is unique about the integral of x^{-1}: It and it alone is not a power of x, but the logarithm of x.

Finally, for the trigonometric functions we find:

$$\frac{d}{dx}(\sin x) = \cos x \rightarrow \int \cos x \, dx = \sin x \qquad (7\text{-}28)$$

$$\frac{d}{dx}(\cos x) = -\sin x \rightarrow \int \sin x \, dx = -\cos x \qquad (7\text{-}29)$$

With the aid of these formulas it is possible to evaluate all the definite integrals encountered in the usual introductory science course. Without the fundamental theorem, the task of finding these formulas (through summation) would have been beyond our capacity.

EXERCISES

1. Using the same type of argument that led us to Eq. 7-4, prove that $\frac{d}{dx}\int_x^b f(x) \, dx = -f(x)$. Prove this also beginning with Eq. 7-4 and using the appropriate integration rule.
2. Prove the rules of integration given in Chapter 5, starting from the rules of differentiation in Chapter 6 and using the Fundamental Theorem.
3. Show that
$$\int f(x)\left[\frac{d}{dx}g(x)\right] dx = f(x)g(x) - \int g(x)\left[\frac{d}{dx}f(x)\right] dx.$$
4. Work out the following indefinite integrals: $4\int dx$; $\int(\frac{1}{2})x \, dx$; $\int x(1 - x) \, dx$; $\int(3x^2 + 4x - 5) \, dx$; $\int 3(x + 1)^2 \, dx$; $\int dx/x^2$; $\int[(x^2 - 2)/x^2] \, dx$.
5. Find: $\int(6x^7 - 10x + 1) \, dx$; $\int(x^2 - x^{-2}) \, dx$; $\int(1 + x^{-1} + x^{-2}) \, dx$; $\int(1 + x)/\sqrt{x} \, dx$.
6. Evaluate the following integrals: $\int_0^{\pi} (\sin x) \, dx$; $\int_0^{\pi/2} (\cos x) \, dx$; $\int_0^{\pi} (\cos x) \, dx$; $\int_{-1}^{+1} e^x \, dx$; $\int_2^e du/u$; $\int_0^1 e^{2t} \, dt$.
7. Write the integral formulas corresponding to the differentiation formulas in Exercise 6-10.

8. What is the total area under the curve $x^2y = 1$ from $x = 1$ on? Draw the curve and shade in the area referred to.

9. Evaluate: $\int_1^x dt/t$; $\int_0^t \sin x \, dx$; $\int_0^t \cos x \, dx$.

10. In a particular chemical reaction, the rate of decrease in the concentration of a substance at any moment is proportional to the concentration at that moment. Express this in symbols, and find the functional relationship between concentration and time.

11. Populations often increase at a rate proportional to their size at any particular time. (This occurs under certain conditions with people, Australian rabbits, and bacteria, to name three examples.) For populations obeying this law of growth, find how their size varies with time.

8

ADDITIONAL TECHNIQUES AND APPLICATIONS[1]

1. THE DERIVATIVE OF A COMPOUND FUNCTION

We know the derivative of sin x with respect to x; we also know the derivative of x^2 with respect to x:

$$\frac{d}{dx} (\sin x) = \cos x$$

$$\frac{d}{dx} x^2 = 2x$$

What if we wanted to find the derivative with respect to x of

[1] For additional material clearly and simply presented, see Sylvanus P. Thompson, *Calculus Made Easy*—subtitled: "Being a Very-Simplest Introduction to those Beautiful Methods of Reckoning which are Generally Called by the Terrifying Names of Differential Calculus and the Integral Calculus"—(New York: Macmillan, 1960).

sin x^2? What would be

$$\frac{d}{dx}(\sin x^2) = ? \tag{8-1}$$

The problem looks as if we should be able to solve it; but we need additional tools to cope with it.

The question we are asking is an example of a broader question. In the case of Eq. 8-1 we have one function, the power function, and another function, the sine function, whose derivatives with respect to x we know, so long as the "arguments" of these functions—i.e., the variables of which they are functions—are simply x. What we want to know is the derivative with respect to x of the sine function, when the argument is in turn a function of x, namely, the power function x^2. Thus, Eq. 8-1 is a special case of the problem of finding the derivative with respect to x of a *compound function*, i.e., of a function whose argument is in turn a function of x. In symbols, if we take $u = x^2$, we are asking for

$$\frac{d}{dx}(\sin u), \qquad \text{where } u = x^2 \tag{8-2}$$

and, in general, if we have y as a function of v, where v is in turn a function of x, the problem is to find

$$\frac{dy}{dx} \qquad \text{where } y = f(v), \text{ and } v = g(x),$$

$$\text{i.e., } \frac{d}{dx}f(v) \text{ where } v = g(x) \tag{8-3}$$

The solution can be most easily found if we make use of what we shall call "the principle of wish fulfillment" as a guide to action. We see that we would have no trouble finding the derivative in question if we were asked for the derivative *with respect to u;* for we know that $d(\sin u)/du = \cos u$. We *wish* the problem would have been to find $d(\sin u)/du$.

Now, the derivative with respect to x is defined as follows (see Chapter 6):

$$\frac{d}{dx} \sin u = \lim_{\Delta x \to 0} \frac{\sin (u + \Delta u) - \sin u}{\Delta x} \tag{8-4}$$

Since we would prefer to find the derivative with respect to u, we would like to have Δu rather than Δx in the denominator on the right. This can be had by multiplying numerator and denominator by Δu and rearranging terms:

$$\frac{d}{dx} \sin u = \lim_{\Delta x \to 0} \frac{\sin (u + \Delta u) - \sin u}{\Delta x} \cdot \frac{\Delta u}{\Delta u}$$

$$= \lim_{\Delta x \to 0} \frac{\sin (u + \Delta u) - \sin u}{\Delta u} \cdot \frac{\Delta u}{\Delta x} \tag{8-5}$$

Using the fact that u is a function of x and that $\Delta u \to 0$ as $\Delta x \to 0$, so that

$$\lim_{\Delta x \to 0}$$

amounts to the same thing as

$$\lim_{\Delta u \to 0}$$

we can rewrite Eq. 8-5 as follows:

$$\frac{d}{dx} \sin u = \lim_{\Delta u \to 0} \frac{\sin (u + \Delta u) - \sin u}{\Delta u} \cdot \lim_{\Delta x \to 0} \frac{\Delta u}{\Delta x}$$

$$= \frac{d}{du} \sin u \cdot \frac{du}{dx} \tag{8-6}$$

(We note by comparing Eqs. 8-5 and 8-6 that Eq. 8-6 tells us simply that in this case, as in all previous cases we have encountered, expressions involving the ratios of finite quantities are replaced by the corresponding ratios of infinitesimals in the limit.) What Eq. 8-6 tells us is that we can follow our wishful thinking, that we can solve the given problem by replacing it with problems whose solutions we know. Specifically, Eq. 8-6 tells us that we can find $d(\sin u)/dx$ by finding first $d(\sin u)/du$, and then multiplying by du/dx, which we also know how to find. In our case, using Eqs. 8-2 and 8-6, we find as the solution to Eq. 8-1,

$$\frac{d}{dx} \sin u = (\cos u)(2x) = (2x)(\cos x^2) \rightarrow$$

$$\frac{d}{dx} \sin x^2 = (2x)(\cos x^2) \tag{8-7}$$

The argument that leads to Eq. 8-6 tells us that the solution to the general problem presented in Eq. 8-3 is:

$$\frac{d}{dx} f(v) = \frac{d}{dv} f(v) \cdot \frac{dv}{dx} \qquad \text{where } v = g(x) \tag{8-8}$$

Let us do one more example. Suppose we ask

$$\frac{d}{dx} [\log (\cos x)] = ? \tag{8-9}$$

Again, we know the derivative of the logarithm and the cosine separately, when the argument is simply x. Our problem is to find

$$\frac{d}{dx} (\log u) \qquad \text{where } u = \cos x \tag{8-10}$$

Proceeding according to Eq. 8-8, and in line with what we know and what we would like to do, we write

$$\frac{d}{dx} (\log u) = \frac{d}{du} (\log u) \cdot \frac{du}{dx}$$

which we can evaluate to be

$$\frac{d}{du} (\log u) \cdot \frac{du}{dx} = \frac{1}{u} \cdot (-\sin x) = \frac{1}{\cos x} (-\sin x)$$

so that the solution of Eq. 8-9 is

$$\frac{d}{dx} [\log (\cos x)] = \frac{-\sin x}{\cos x} = -\tan x \tag{8-11}$$

In general, the way to cope with compound functions is to reduce the problem to functions and derivatives *with which we are familiar;* and, in making this reduction, we can check that we are on the right track by treating quotients of infinitesimals as if they were quotients of finite magnitudes.

2. DIFFERENTIALS

The derivative dy/dx at point P is the ratio of the magnitudes of infinitesimal increments in y and x, respectively, for y and x related by some functional relationship $y = f(x)$. This ratio, as we have seen, is the limit of the ratio of *finite* increments Δy and Δx, as $\Delta x \to 0$; except for the case of a straight line, dy/dx and $\Delta y/\Delta x$ always differ, since the former refers to an infinitesimal interval on the curve (or, alternatively, to the slope of the straight line tangent to the curve at P), while the latter refers to a finite interval on the curve (see Fig. 8-1): dy/dx and $\Delta y/\Delta x$ differ by

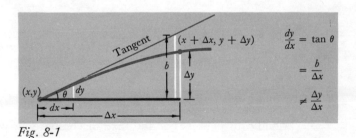

Fig. 8-1

an amount that depends on how far the second point [with coordinates $(x + \Delta x, y + \Delta y)$] is distant from the first, and how "curved" the curve is—i.e., how much the curve deviates from the tangent. The smaller the finite increments Δy, Δx are, the closer dy/dx and $\Delta y/\Delta x$ will be.

These elementary considerations lead to an extremely useful

practical result: For sufficiently small increments, the "differentials" dy and dx can be used as good approximations of the "finite differences" Δy and Δx, and, in particular, the ratio dy/dx—the derivative—can be used to approximate the ratio of finite differences $\Delta y/\Delta x$. Such approximations make it possible for us to obtain quick estimates of answers we need, without going to the trouble of lengthy calculations or tedious searches in tables. For example, suppose we wanted to get an idea of how big $(10.1)^3$ is. We are dealing with the function $y = x^3$, and we know the value of y for $x = 10$ (namely, $y = 10^3 = 1,000$). What we want is the amount by which $y = x^3$ increases when x increases from 10.0 to 10.1—i.e., for $\Delta x = 0.1$. If the increments were *infinitesimal*, their ratio at the point in question would be $(dy/dx)_{(10,1000)} = (3x^2)_{(10,1000)} = 3 \times 10^2 = 300$. If we now assume that the ratio of finite increments is just about equal to this, we obtain

$$\left(\frac{\Delta y}{\Delta x}\right)_{(10,1000)} \sim \left(\frac{dy}{dx}\right)_{(10,1000)} = 300 \rightarrow \Delta y \sim 300 \, \Delta x$$

$$(8\text{-}12)$$

which, for $\Delta x = 0.1$, yields

$$\Delta y \sim 300 \times 0.1 = 30 \rightarrow (10.1)^3 = (10 + 0.1)^3$$
$$\sim (10)^3 + \Delta y = 1000 + 30 = 1030 \qquad (8\text{-}13)$$

This is to be compared with the exact answer: $(10.1)^3 = 1030.301$; the approximation in Eq. 8-13 is seen to be valid up to four significant figures. For the sake of comparison, we can attempt to use Eq. 8-12 to evaluate $(11)^3$ and $(10.01)^3$. In the first case, for $(11)^3$, we have

$$\Delta x = 1, \Delta y \sim 300\Delta x = 300 \rightarrow (11)^3 = (10 + 1)^3$$
$$\sim (10)^3 + \Delta y = 1000 + 300 = 1300 \qquad (8\text{-}14)$$

to be compared with the exact answer: $(11)^3 = 1331$; here the approximation is good to two significant figures. In the second case, for $(10.01)^3$, we have

$$\Delta x = 0.01, \Delta y \sim 300\Delta x = 3 \rightarrow (10.01)^3 = (10 + 0.01)^3$$
$$\sim(10)^3 + \Delta y = 1003 \qquad\qquad (8\text{-}15)$$

to be compared with the exact answer: $(10.01)^3 = 1003.003001$; here the approximation holds to six significant figures. The example shows clearly how the closeness of the approximation varies with the size of the increment, becoming greater as the increment considered becomes smaller.

It must always be remembered that

$$\frac{\Delta y}{\Delta x} \sim \frac{dy}{dx} \qquad\qquad (8\text{-}16)$$

is an approximation and not an equality; if this is borne in mind Eq. 8-16 can be used to great advantage in making assessments of finite changes with the aid of the derivative.

3. THE INTEGRAL OF A COMPOUND FUNCTION. CHANGE OF VARIABLE

The problem of integrating compound functions is similar in nature to that of differentiating compound functions: Both find their solution in use of the "principle of wish fulfillment." The idea is to try to change the form of the integral from the one that is given to the one that we know.

Consider, for example, the following case. We want to know

$$\int \cos kx\, dx = ? \qquad \text{(where } k \text{ is a constant)} \qquad (8\text{-}17)$$

What we do know from our table of integrals is

$$\int \cos u\, du = \sin u \qquad\qquad (8\text{-}18)$$

but Eq. 8-17 is not quite the same, since the factor k has intruded into the cosine function: The cosine no longer has the variable alone as an argument; instead, the cosine is a function of the argument (kx), i.e., a function of the function $v = kx$. In other words, Eq. 8-17 actually has the form

$$\int \cos v \, dx = ? \quad \text{for } v = kx \quad (8\text{-}19)$$

To get Eq. 8-19 to be like Eq. 8-18, we must change dx to dv in the integrand of Eq. 8-19—i.e., we must change the *variable of integration* from x to v. We can do this if we know the relationship between the differentials dv and dx. But we know the functional relationship between v and x $(v = kx)$, so that we know the derivative dv/dx and hence the ratio of the differentials. Thus,

$$\frac{dv}{dx} = k \quad \rightarrow \quad dv = k \, dx \quad (8\text{-}20)$$

We can thus replace dx by dv/k in the integrand, obtaining

$$\int \cos v \, dx = \int \cos v \, dv/k = (1/k)\int \cos v \, dv$$
$$= (1/k) \sin v \quad \text{for } v = kx \quad (8\text{-}21)$$

Thus, we find that

$$\int \cos kx \, dx = (1/k) \sin kx \quad (8\text{-}22)$$

and Eq. 8-17 is answered.

This example illustrates the general method by which one can attempt to integrate compound functions: A change of variable is made with the aim of bringing the integral into a familiar form. Such attempts will not always be successful, as the exercises will show, but where they do succeed, they make integration possible.

4. SECOND AND HIGHER DERIVATIVES

We have seen that the derivative of a function of x is itself a function of x. Thus, the derivative of $y = x^2$ is $dy/dx = 2x$, which is a linear function of x.[2] Viewed as a new function of x, the derivative can in turn be differentiated. In our example, we can differentiate the function $2x$, obtaining $d(2x)/dx = 2$; here, the derivative of the derivative turns out to be 2.[3]

In general, we can always differentiate the derivative and go on differentiating the derivative of the derivative, etc. The derivative of the derivative is referred to as the *second derivative*, denoted by

$$\frac{d}{dx}\left(\frac{dy}{dx}\right) \equiv \frac{d^2y}{dx^2} \equiv f''(x) \tag{8-23}$$

The derivative of Eq. 8-23 is called the *third derivative* and is denoted by

$$\frac{d}{dx}\left(\frac{d^2y}{dx^2}\right) \equiv \frac{d^3y}{dx^3} \equiv f'''(x) \tag{8-24}$$

and so forth for derivatives of this, in turn. Often, derivatives other than the first are referred to as *higher derivatives* of the function.

Higher derivatives of a function convey information about the function. We will discuss only the case of the second derivative, as this finds widespread use.

---

[2] The statement holds also for $y = ax$, in which case the derivative $dy/dx = a$ is a *constant* function of x.

[3] The fact that the derivative $dy/dx = f'(x)$ is itself a function of x is what led Lagrange to introduce the name "derivative": he viewed $f'(x)$ as a "derived function" ("fonction dérivée"), i.e., a function *derived* from the original function $f(x)$.

When we differentiate a function, we find the rate of change of the function with respect to the independent variable. When we differentiate the derivative, we find the rate of change of the *derivative* (i.e., the rate of change of the rate of change) with respect to the independent variable. Loosely speaking, the second derivative tells us how fast the rate of change is changing. We use this concept often in our everyday experience. For example, when we speak of inflation, we are usually interested in the following three things: (1) The actual level of the price index at any given time. This is the basic function, and the variables are the index i and time t. (2) The rate of inflation—i.e., the rate of change (in this case, *rise*) of the price index ("the index is rising at the rate of 1.2% per year"). This rate at any particular time is the derivative di/dt. (3) How the rate of inflation is changing with time ("the inflation rate has been slowing down in recent years, from 3.1% three years ago to 1.2% last year; it is currently slowing down by 1% each year"). This is the derivative of the inflation rate, or the second derivative of the index, d^2i/dt^2. All three concepts can be visualized by looking at the graph of the index versus time (see Fig. 8-2). The actual height of the curve

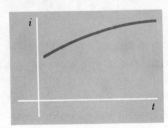

Fig. 8-2

gives the index at any time; the slope gives the inflation rate; and the change in slope—in this case, the slope becoming less and less steep with time—gives the change in inflation rate.

The many applications of the second derivative are all basically similar to the simple example we have just discussed.

5. CURVE TRACING. MAXIMA AND MINIMA

Knowledge of the first and second derivatives of a function enables us to draw a rough graph of the function—to get an idea of the shape of the curve, without going to the trouble of plotting a whole series of points. This can be seen if we consider the following simple properties of these derivatives:

1. Where the (first) derivative is positive, the slope of the tangent to the curve is positive, which means that the curve is *rising*. Where the derivative is negative, the curve is *descending*:

$$\left.\begin{array}{l} \dfrac{dy}{dx} > 0 \rightarrow \text{curve rising} \\[2mm] \dfrac{dy}{dx} < 0 \rightarrow \text{curve descending} \end{array}\right\} \qquad (8\text{-}25)$$

2. Where the derivative is 0, the tangent is horizontal. This means that we are at either a local maximum, a local minimum, or a horizontal point of inflection (see Fig. 8-3).[4]

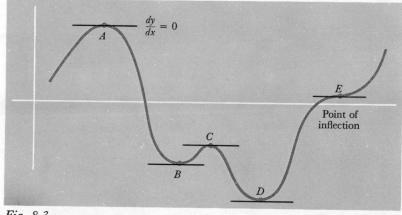

Fig. 8-3

---

[4] At a point of inflection the curve has an S-shape and hence can have no tangent in the sense we have been using, inasmuch as the line "just touching" the curve must also intersect it. Nevertheless, the line "just touching" is still called the tangent.

The word "local" is important, as can be seen from the figure. The point B is obviously not the lowest point on the entire curve, so it cannot be called "the" minimum. But it is lower than all neighboring points, and is a "local" minimum on the curve. Thus,

$$\frac{dy}{dx} = 0 \rightarrow \begin{cases} \text{local maximum, minimum,} \\ \text{or horizontal point of} \\ \text{inflection} \end{cases} \qquad (8\text{-}26)$$

3. Where the *second* derivative is positive, the rate of change of the first derivative with respect to x is positive—i.e., the first derivative is increasing with increasing x. In other words, where d^2y/dx^2 is positive, the slope of the tangent gets larger (i.e., more positive) as x does: If the slope is negative it becomes less negative, and if the slope is positive it becomes more positive, with increasing x. The curve is therefore *concave upward*, since only a curve concave upward has a slope increasing from left to right (see Fig. 8-4(a)). Where the second derivative is negative, the curve is concave downward (Fig. 8-4(b)):

$$\left. \begin{array}{l} \dfrac{d^2y}{dx^2} > 0 \rightarrow \text{curve concave upward} \\[3mm] \dfrac{d^2y}{dx^2} < 0 \rightarrow \text{curve concave downward} \end{array} \right\} \qquad (8\text{-}27)$$

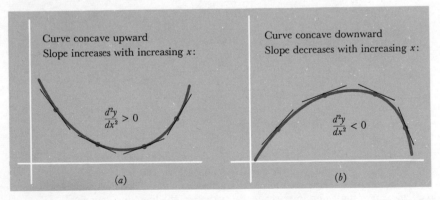

Curve concave upward
Slope increases with increasing x:

$$\frac{d^2y}{dx^2} > 0$$

Curve concave downward
Slope decreases with increasing x:

$$\frac{d^2y}{dx^2} < 0$$

(a)   (b)

Fig. 8-4

4. Where the second derivative is zero, the slope itself has reached its (local) maximum or minimum, and we are either in a flat section of the curve, or in a place where the curve is changing from concave upward to concave downward—called a "point of inflection" (Fig. 8-5).

$$\frac{d^2y}{dx^2} = 0 \rightarrow \left\{ \begin{array}{l} \text{flat portion or point} \\ \text{of inflection} \end{array} \right. \qquad (8\text{-}28)$$

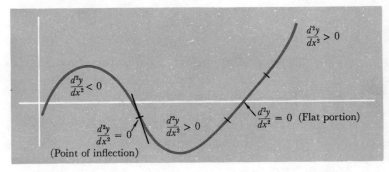

Fig. 8-5

To give an example of how these four properties help us to trace a curve, consider the graph of the function

$$y = 4x^3 - 6x^2 + 2 \qquad (8\text{-}29)$$

Finding y values corresponding to various x values is obviously tedious, and drawing the curve accurately would require a large number of pairs. Let us instead find and study the derivatives

$$\frac{dy}{dx} = 12x^2 - 12x = 12x(x - 1) \qquad (8\text{-}30)$$

$$\frac{d}{dx}\left(\frac{dy}{dx}\right) = \frac{d^2y}{dx^2} = 24x - 12 = 12(2x - 1) \qquad (8\text{-}31)$$

From Eq. 8-30 we find:

$$\frac{dy}{dx} = 0 \text{ where } 12x(x - 1) = 0; \text{ i.e., where } x = 0 \text{ and } x = 1$$
$$(8\text{-}32)$$

Substituting into Eq. 8-29, we find that there are local maxima or minima or horizontal points of inflection at (0,2) and (1,0). In addition, we see from Eq. 8-30 that

$$\frac{dy}{dx} > 0 \text{ where } 12x(x - 1) > 0; \text{ i.e., where } x > 1 \text{ or } x < 0$$

$$(8\text{-}33)$$

$$\frac{dy}{dx} < 0 \text{ where } 0 < x < 1 \qquad\qquad (8\text{-}34)$$

This is already sufficient to tell us that the curve rises up to the point (0,2), then descends to (1,0), and then goes on rising again. From Eq. 8-31 we see that

$$\frac{d^2y}{dx^2} > 0 \text{ where } 12(2x - 1) > 0; \text{ i.e., where } x > \tfrac{1}{2}$$

$$(8\text{-}35)$$

$$\frac{d^2y}{dx^2} < 0 \text{ where } x < \tfrac{1}{2} \qquad\qquad (8\text{-}36)$$

$$\frac{d^2y}{dx^2} = 0 \text{ where } x = \tfrac{1}{2} \qquad\qquad (8\text{-}37)$$

From these results we learn that the curve is concave downward up to $x = \tfrac{1}{2}$, then has a point of inflection and changes to concave upward thereafter. With this information at our disposal, we can sketch the curve that is illustrated in Fig. 8-6. (Greater accuracy can of course be attained if we find a few x, y pairs lying on the curve to serve as anchor points, so to speak. This is still far less arduous than plotting the entire curve by finding individual pairs.)

Use of the derivative to trace curves, and to find local maxima and minima (and points of inflection), is a considerable convenience and a useful technique on many occasions.

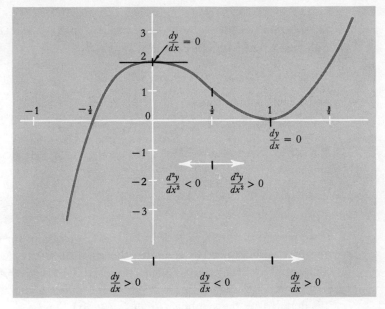

Fig. 8-6

6. PARTIAL DERIVATIVES.
TOTAL DIFFERENTIALS

What if we are dealing with more than two variables? In particular, suppose we have three variables, two independent (x and y) and one dependent (z), such that to every pair of values x, y chosen at will there corresponds a value of z:

$$z = f(x,y) \qquad\qquad (8\text{-}38)$$

This means that we have *triplets* of related values, (x_1,y_1,z_1), related by $z_1 = f(x_1,y_1)$. Now there are a number of ways z_1 can change. For example, the y-value, y_1, can be left unchanged, and the x-value can be changed by Δx. This will change z_1 to some other value, which we will denote by $(z_1 + \Delta z)_y$, the subscript indicating that y is kept constant. By Eq. 8-38,

$$(z_1 + \Delta z)_y = f(x_1 + \Delta x, y_1) \tag{8-39}$$

and hence, subtracting,

$$(\Delta z)_y = f(x_1 + \Delta x, y_1) - f(x_1, y_1) \tag{8-40}$$

We can now proceed as before, always regarding y as a constant, and form

$$\left(\frac{\Delta z}{\Delta x}\right)_y = \frac{f(x_1 + \Delta x, y_1) - f(x_1, y_1)}{\Delta x} \tag{8-41}$$

If we pass to the limit $\Delta x \to 0$ in Eq. 8-41, we obtain the derivative of z with respect to x, under the condition that y remains constant. This derivative is called "the partial derivative of z with respect to x," the word "partial" denoting that x alone changes; it is denoted by the symbols $(\partial z/\partial x)_y$, $(\partial f/\partial x)_y$, or f_x:

$$\left(\frac{\partial z}{\partial x}\right)_y \equiv \left(\frac{\partial f}{\partial x}\right)_y \equiv f_x \equiv \lim_{\Delta x \to 0} \left(\frac{\Delta z}{\Delta x}\right)_y$$
$$= \lim_{\Delta x \to 0} \frac{f(x + \Delta x, y) - f(x, y)}{\Delta x} \tag{8-42}$$

where we have dropped the subscript "1," since the definition is valid for any triplet related by Eq. 8-38.

Essentially, then, by holding the other variable(s) constant, the partial derivative with respect to x treats the function as if its only *variable* were x.

Another way z can change is by holding x constant and allowing only y to change. This gives, by strict analogy to the preceding discussion, the partial derivative with respect to y:

$$\left(\frac{\partial z}{\partial y}\right)_x \equiv \left(\frac{\partial f}{\partial y}\right)_x \equiv f_y \equiv \lim_{\Delta y \to 0} \left(\frac{\Delta z}{\Delta y}\right)_x$$
$$\equiv \lim_{\Delta y \to 0} \frac{f(x, y + \Delta y) - f(x, y)}{\Delta y} \tag{8-43}$$

A third way z can change is by allowing *both x and y* to change. In this case, none of the variables is held constant, and the change in the function z is given by

$$\Delta z = f(x + \Delta x, y + \Delta y) - f(x,y) \tag{8-44}$$

In the limit as $\Delta x \to 0$ and $\Delta y \to 0$, we obtain the infinitesimal change dz corresponding to infinitesimal changes dx and dy:

$$\begin{aligned} dz &= \lim_{\Delta x, \, \Delta y \to 0} \Delta z \\ &= \lim_{\Delta x, \, \Delta y \to 0} \{ f(x + \Delta x, y + \Delta y) - f(x,y) \} \end{aligned} \tag{8-45}$$

To get the right-hand side to look more familiar, we add and subtract a term which makes it possible to treat the changes in x and y independently:

$$\begin{aligned} &\lim_{\Delta x, \, \Delta y \to 0} \{ f(x + \Delta x, y + \Delta y) - f(x,y) \} \\ &= \lim_{\Delta x, \, \Delta y \to 0} \{ f(x + \Delta x, y + \Delta y) \\ &\quad - f(x, y + \Delta y) + f(x, y + \Delta y) - f(x,y) \} \end{aligned} \tag{8-46}$$

Now, by Eq. 8-43, we have

$$\begin{aligned} &\lim_{\Delta y \to 0} \{ f(x, y + \Delta y) - f(x,y) \} \\ &= \lim_{\Delta y \to 0} \left\{ \frac{f(x, y + \Delta y) - f(x,y)}{\Delta y} \cdot \Delta y \right\} \\ &= \lim_{\Delta y \to 0} \left\{ \frac{f(x, y + \Delta y) - f(x,y)}{\Delta y} \right\} \cdot \lim_{\Delta y \to 0} \Delta y \\ &= \left(\frac{\partial z}{\partial y} \right)_x dy \end{aligned} \tag{8-47}$$

where we recall that

$$\lim_{\Delta y \to 0} \Delta y = dy$$

Similarly, by Eq. 8-42 we have

$$
\begin{aligned}
\lim_{\Delta x,\,\Delta y\to 0} & \{f(x + \Delta x, y + \Delta y) - f(x, y + \Delta y)\} \\
= & \lim_{\Delta x\to 0} \{f(x + \Delta x, y) - f(x,y)\} \\
= & \lim_{\Delta x\to 0} \left\{ \frac{f(x + \Delta x, y) - f(x,y)}{\Delta x} \right\} \cdot \lim_{\Delta x\to 0} \Delta x \\
= & \left(\frac{\partial z}{\partial x}\right)_y dx \qquad\qquad\qquad (8\text{-}48)
\end{aligned}
$$

Combining Eqs. 8-48 and 8-47 in Eq. 8-45, we find for the "total differential of z" the expression

$$
dz = \left(\frac{\partial z}{\partial x}\right)_y dx + \left(\frac{\partial z}{\partial y}\right)_x dy
$$

for $z = f(x,y)$; or

$$
df = \left(\frac{\partial f}{\partial x}\right)_y dx + \left(\frac{\partial f}{\partial y}\right)_x dy \equiv f_x\, dx + f_y\, dy \qquad (8\text{-}49)
$$

These expressions enable us to cope with all possible changes in a function of more than one variable, i.e., with changes in which only one variable changes, the others remaining constant, or with changes in which all the variables change. The expressions have geometrical interpretations that are interesting, but they are beyond the scope of this book; they can be found in all standard textbooks.

There is an interesting by-product of Eq. 8-49 that is worth noting before concluding this section. Equation 8-49 relates infinitesimal increments, dx, dy, and dz, with the aid of two partial derivatives as coefficients. Suppose we consider the special case $dz = 0$; for this special choice of dz, Eq. 8-49 becomes a relation between infinitesimal increments in x and y when z is unchanged, i.e., when z is held constant:

$$
0 = \left(\frac{\partial z}{\partial x}\right)_y (dx)_z + \left(\frac{\partial z}{\partial y}\right)_x (dy)_z \qquad (8\text{-}50)
$$

where we have used the notation introduced earlier. Regrouping this, we find:

$$\left(\frac{\partial z}{\partial x}\right)_y \left(\frac{\partial x}{\partial y}\right)_z = -\left(\frac{\partial z}{\partial y}\right)_x, \text{ or}$$

$$\left(\frac{\partial z}{\partial x}\right)_y \left(\frac{\partial x}{\partial y}\right)_z \left(\frac{\partial y}{\partial z}\right)_x = -1 \qquad (8\text{-}51)$$

Equation 8-51 relates the three different partial derivatives that can be formed from $z = f(x,y)$; Eq. 8-51 is surprising in that the right-hand side has a negative sign, while for finite quotients the expressions on the left side would have all cancelled and left the result $+1$. We have thus come across our first case in which differential quotients do not behave like finite quotients. In fact, whenever we are dealing with partial derivatives we must exercise special care not to take it for granted that we can treat them like finite quotients.

EXERCISES

1. Differentiate the following: $y = \log (\log x)$; $y = e^{-x^2}$; $y = e^{-kx^2}$; $y = x^x$ (use the fact that $x^x = e^{x \log x}$).
2. Differentiate: $x \sin (x^2)$; $\cos (3x^2 + 5)$; $\log \sin x$; $\log (1 + x)$; $\log (1 + x^2)$; $e^{\log x}$.
3. What is the integration formula corresponding to the derivative in Eq. 8-11?
4. Using differentials, compute the approximate values of: $\sqrt{99}$; $\sqrt[3]{215}$; $\log 10.2$ (given that $\log 10 = 2.3026$).
5. What is an approximate expression for $\sqrt{1 \pm \alpha}$ when α is very small? for $1/\sqrt{1 \pm \alpha}$?
6. Find the derivative and integral of e^{kx}, considering it as a compound function. Compare with the results found in Chapters 6 and 7.
7. Find the following integrals, where you can, by changing variables: $\int (a + bx)^{\frac{3}{2}} dx$; $\int \sin (x^2) dx$; $\int x \cos (x^2) dx$;

$$\int \frac{dx}{1 + x}; \int \frac{dx}{2 + 3x}; \int \sqrt{1 - 2x}\, dx; \int e^{x^2} dx; \int x e^{x^2} dx.$$

8. Evaluate the following integrals by making appropriate changes in the variables: $\int_{-1}^{-3} (x + 2)^8 \, dx$; $\int_0^4 e^{-4x^2} x \, dx$.

9. Discuss how a change of variable in a definite integral can be viewed as a change in width of the strips into which the area is partitioned.

10. Find the first and second derivatives of the following functions: $1/x^3$; $\sin(x^2)$; $(x - 1)/(x + 1)$; $\cos 3x$; $x \sin x + \cos x$; e^{3x}.

11. Show that the first and all higher derivatives of $y = e^{-x^2}$ have the form e^{-x^2} multiplied by a monomial or a polynomial.

12. Find the maxima and minima of: $y = \sin x$; $y = \cos x$; $y = \sin x^2$.

13. Find the local maxima and minima of the following: $y = \sin 2x - x$; $y = 1 - x - e^{-2x}$; $y = x^2 e^x$.

14. Sketch the graphs of the following functions: $f(x) = 2x^3 - 9x^2 + 12x + 1$; $f(x) = (x^2 - 1)(x^2 - 4)$; $f(x) = x + 1/x$.

15. Discuss and explain in detail statement Number 4 in Section 5 (the statement that includes Eq. 8-28).

16. Given the relation $pV = aT$, where a is a constant, find: $(\partial T/\partial V)_p$; $(\partial T/\partial p)_V$; dT; $(\partial p/\partial V)_T$; $(\partial p/\partial T)_V$; $(\partial V/\partial T)_p$.

17. Consider the function $f(x,y) = xy$. Find $(\partial f/\partial x)_y$, $(\partial f/\partial y)_x$, $(\partial^2 f/\partial x^2)_y$, $(\partial^2 f/\partial y^2)_x$, $(\partial^2 f/\partial x \, \partial y)$, $(\partial^2 f/\partial y \, \partial x)$. [The fact that the last two derivatives are equal is an instance of a general theorem stating that $(\partial^2 f/\partial x \, \partial y) = (\partial^2 f/\partial y \, \partial x)$ for a wide class of functions.]

18. For the function $f(x,y,z) = 1/\sqrt{x^2 + y^2 + z^2}$, find f_x, f_y, f_z, and show that $f_{xx} + f_{yy} + f_{zz} = 0$ is obeyed for all values of (x,y,z) [except for $(0,0,0)$, where the expressions for the partial derivatives, as well as for the function itself, are meaningless].

PART III

VECTORS

9

ELEMENTARY
VECTOR
ALGEBRA

1. SCALARS

Most of the things with which science deals can be measured. Whatever part of nature is being studied, science aims to quantify it, to express its properties and behavior in terms of measurable quantities.

Certain measurable entities can be fully specified by a single number—a number that gives their magnitude or size, telling how many basic units they contain. (Of course, along with the number, the particular basic units being used must also be given.) For example, a length can be fully specified by a single number that represents the number of basic units of length (centimeters or meters or inches or some other units) it contains; a population can be fully specified by the number of basic units it contains (mice or human beings or American males or some other units, depending on the study being made); and so forth. Quantities of this sort are called *scalars*, since they are fully describable by a point on a scale, i.e., by a single number that tells their scale or size.

Many measurable entities are not scalars. For example, traffic flow at Fifth Avenue and Forty-Second Street in New York is not a scalar, since a single number does not suffice to specify it (Fig. 9-1). Instead two numbers are needed, one to denote

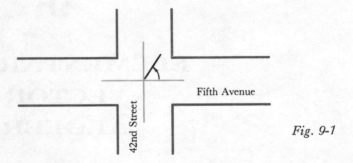

Fifth Avenue

42nd Street

Fig. 9-1

the magnitude of flow (in, say, *cars per hour*) and the other to denote the direction of flow (in, say, *degrees*, measured relative to Fifth Avenue as the base line). The two numbers *together* do specify traffic flow: There is a certain magnitude of flow in the 0° direction, a certain magnitude of flow in the 90° direction, and a certain magnitude of flow in the 180° and 270° directions— and, hopefully, there will be zero magnitude of flow in any other direction.

Another example of a measurable entity that is not a scalar is the result of an experiment in which gray male mice are bred with gray female mice, where each of the gray mice is the hybrid offspring of a pure white and pure black parent. The result of such an experiment cannot be fully specified by a single number and hence is not a scalar. One of the most convenient ways to specify the result is by means of an array of numbers, arranged according to the skin-color trait inherited from each of the parents. For example, from the array shown in Table 9-1 we can see that of 800 offspring, 200 inherited the white skin-color trait from both parents (and hence were white), 200 inherited the black skin-color trait from both parents (and hence were black), and 400 inherited the white trait from one parent and the black trait from the other (and hence were gray).

Table 9-1   Results of Breeding Experiment in Which Every Parent Was a Gray Hybrid of Pure White and Pure Black, so That Each Parent Transmitted to the Offspring White and Black Skin-Color Traits with Equal Probability

	White skin-color trait inherited from mother	Black skin-color trait inherited from mother
White skin-color trait inherited from father	200	200
Black skin-color trait inherited from father	200	200

Scalars are the easiest quantities to handle. However, the physical and natural sciences also deal very often with quantities like that illustrated in the traffic-flow example, and we shall devote this chapter and the next two chapters to the study of such quantities, called *vectors*.[1]

[1] Various branches of science also have a great deal of use for *tensors*, *spinors*, and *matrices*, which are arrays of numbers having certain specific properties. We will not be concerned with such entities, since they are useful in areas that are more advanced than those generally studied in introductory science courses.

2. VECTORS

A vector is a *directed magnitude*, a quantity fully specified by both a magnitude and a direction. A vector will always be denoted in this book by a boldface letter, e.g., **a**, **B**. It will be represented pictorially by a directed line segment, i.e., by a line segment whose length represents the magnitude of the vector and whose direction (as indicated by an arrowhead attached to the segment) is the direction of the vector (Fig. 9-2). The magnitude of a

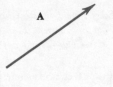

Fig. 9-2

A vector

vector will be denoted either by a letter printed in ordinary typeface (*A*) or by a boldface letter enclosed in an absolute-value sign ($|\mathbf{A}|$).

In two dimensions, two numbers are required to specify a vector fully: one number to specify the magnitude (in whatever units are chosen for the quantity being considered), and a second number to specify the angle (in radians, for example) made by the vector relative to a fixed reference direction. In three dimensions, three numbers are required to specify a vector fully: one number to specify the magnitude, and *two* additional numbers to specify the direction—for example, an *azimuthal angle* ϕ, which is the angle between the vector's projection onto a plane and some fixed reference direction in the plane, and an *angle of inclination* θ, the angle through which the vector is depressed below the vertical to the plane (see Fig. 9-3). In general, as many numbers are required to specify a vector fully as there are dimensions: one number for the magnitude, the remaining numbers for the direction.

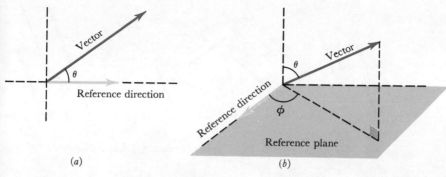

Fig. 9-3   (a) Vector in two dimensions. (b) Vector in three dimensions.

A *zero* or *null* vector is a vector of zero magnitude. For such a vector no direction can be specified, so that the direction of a null vector is indeterminate. A null vector is denoted by **0**.

The *negative* of a vector (Fig. 9-4) is another vector of equal magnitude and opposite direction.[2]

Fig. 9-4   *The negative of a vector.*

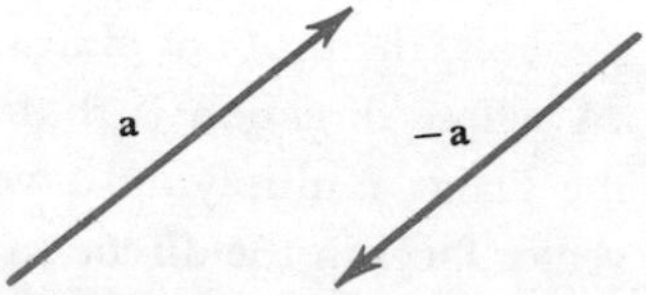

Two vectors are *equal* if and only if they have equal magnitudes *and* the same direction. The vectors shown in Fig. 9-5(a) are all equal to one another. On the other hand, no two of the vectors shown in Fig. 9-5(b) and (c), are equal; in (b) the magnitudes of all the vectors are the same but the directions are all different from one another, while in (c) the directions of all the vectors are the same but the magnitudes are all different from one another.

[2] The negative of a vector is defined in this way because, according to the rules of vector addition to be discussed ahead, the sum of a vector and its negative is the null vector $(\mathbf{A} + [-\mathbf{A}] = \mathbf{0})$. Thus, the negative of a vector in vector algebra corresponds to the negative of a number in ordinary algebra.

Fig. 9-5   (a) Equal vectors. (b) Unequal vectors. (c) Unequal vectors.

3. UNIT VECTORS

When a vector is multiplied by a positive scalar (a positive number), the result is a new vector having the same direction as the original vector and having a magnitude which is the product of the scalar and the magnitude of the original vector. In symbols, the product of a scalar a and a vector **A** is a new vector a**A** whose direction is that of **A** and whose magnitude is aA. If the scalar multiplying a vector is a negative number, the new vector faces in the direction opposite to that of the original vector (Fig. 9-6).

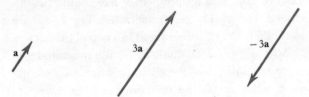

Fig. 9-6   Product of a scalar and a vector.

The rules for multiplying a scalar and a vector enable us to introduce the concept of a *unit vector*, which often leads to considerable simplification in calculations involving vectors. As the name suggests, a unit vector in a particular direction is a vector of *unit magnitude* pointing in that direction; it is denoted by a boldface letter with a caret over it ($\hat{\mathbf{e}}$). If, now, $\hat{\mathbf{e}}$ is a unit vector in a given direction, then *any* vector $\mathbf{A}$ in that direction can be expressed as the product of the unit vector $\hat{\mathbf{e}}$ and a positive scalar equal to the magnitude of $\mathbf{A}$ (since the magnitude of $\hat{\mathbf{e}}$ is unity):

$$\mathbf{A} = A\hat{\mathbf{e}} \qquad \text{(where } \mathbf{A} \parallel \hat{\mathbf{e}}) \tag{9-1}$$

In addition, *any* vector $\mathbf{B}$ facing in the direction opposite to that of $\hat{\mathbf{e}}$ can be expressed as the product of the vector $\hat{\mathbf{e}}$ and a negative scalar equal to the negative of the magnitude of $\mathbf{B}$:

$$\mathbf{B} = -B\hat{\mathbf{e}} \qquad \text{(where } \mathbf{B} \text{ anti- } \parallel \hat{\mathbf{e}}) \tag{9-2}$$

When a vector is written with the aid of the unit vector, as in Eqs. 9-1 and 9-2, the two aspects of the vector, magnitude and direction, are separately displayed. The magnitude is displayed as a scalar multiplying the unit vector, and the direction is given by the direction of the unit vector (being either parallel or anti-parallel to $\hat{\mathbf{e}}$, according to the sign before the product).[3]

4. ADDITION OF VECTORS

Given two vectors $\mathbf{A}$ and $\mathbf{B}$, the *sum* of these two vectors, $\mathbf{A} + \mathbf{B} \equiv \mathbf{C}$, is defined according to the following operations: place the tail of $\mathbf{B}$ at the head of $\mathbf{A}$; then find the vector whose tail is at the tail of $\mathbf{A}$ and whose head is at the head of $\mathbf{B}$; this

---

[3] The role of the unit vector is analogous to the role of the imaginary unit i in the theory of imaginary numbers. The square root of any negative number is imaginary. By introducing the imaginary unit $i = \sqrt{-1}$, all imaginary numbers can be expressed as the product of a real number and the imaginary unit, thus displaying separately the two aspects of an imaginary number, its "magnitude" and its "imaginariness."

Fig. 9-7   Vector addition.

vector is $\mathbf{C} \equiv \mathbf{A} + \mathbf{B}$ (Fig. 9-7). The result of vector addition does not depend on the order of the factors: The sum $\mathbf{B} + \mathbf{A}$ is the same as the sum $\mathbf{A} + \mathbf{B}$. This is true because both $\mathbf{A} + \mathbf{B}$ and $\mathbf{B} + \mathbf{A}$ are the diagonal of the parallelogram whose sides are $\mathbf{A}$ and $\mathbf{B}$ (Fig. 9-8). The fact that vector addition does not

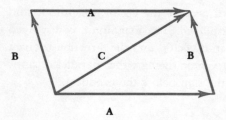

Fig.   9-8   Commutative   law   for vector addition.

depend on the order of the factors is expressed by saying that vector addition is *commutative*.

The addition of three or more vectors is accomplished by adding the first two, then adding their sum to the third, and so proceeding until all the vectors have been added. The same resultant sum can be obtained by taking all the vectors to be added and joining them head to tail; their vector sum will then be the vector connecting the free tail (of the first vector in the sum) to the free head (of the last vector in the sum—see Fig. 9-9).

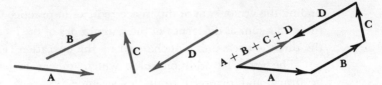

Fig. 9-9   Sum of four vectors.

When three or more vectors are added, it makes no difference whether (or how) some are grouped together and added
first, and then added to the others. In other words, $(\mathbf{A} + \mathbf{B}) +$
$\mathbf{C} = \mathbf{A} + (\mathbf{B} + \mathbf{C}) = \mathbf{A} + \mathbf{B} + \mathbf{C}$. This is expressed by saying
that vector addition is *associative*.

In order to *subtract* a vector **B** from a vector **A**, we *add* the
vector $-\mathbf{B}$ to **A**. Thus, to find $\mathbf{C} \equiv \mathbf{A} - \mathbf{B}$, we use the fact that
$\mathbf{A} - \mathbf{B} = \mathbf{A} + (-\mathbf{B})$ (Fig. 9-10).

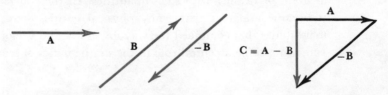

Fig. 9-10   Vector subtraction.

Generally, the sum of two vectors is not in the same direction
as either of the vectors, and the magnitude of the sum is not the
sum of the magnitudes of the factors.[4] Thus, generally, finding
sums or differences is a more complicated operation for vectors
than for scalars, except in the special case when the factors in
the vector sum are parallel; in that case, and in that case alone,

[4] This is true because of the *triangle inequality*, which states that the sum
of the lengths of two sides of a triangle is always greater than the length of
the third side (and two vectors and their sum form, in general, a triangle).
See E. Beckenbach and R. Bellman, *An Introduction to Inequalities* (New York:
Random House, 1961), a small paperback book for nonspecialists, written
in a comprehensible style without sacrificing mathematical rigor.

finding the vector sum or difference reduces in practice to finding the scalar sum or difference of the magnitudes of the factors, with the direction remaining unchanged by the operation (Fig. 9-11).

The vectorial addition rules, which appear to be entirely arbitrary and divorced from "experience," were actually ab-

A   B   A + B

Fig. 9-11   Addition of parallel vectors.

stracted from experience with certain physical quantities that, like vectors, are specified by direction and magnitude. The rules for addition were modeled after the way physical forces were observed to combine; in turn, calculations with forces were greatly simplified once techniques were developed and standardized for dealing with such quantities. In the course of time, it became apparent that many physical entities were directed magnitudes that combined the way forces do, and vector algebra came to assume a central role in the mathematics of science.

5. VECTORS IN A PLANE. THE STANDARD DECOMPOSITION

Consider an arbitrary vector **R** in a plane. We can *always* express **R** as the sum of two other vectors in the plane, *whose directions may be specified at will, so long as the two vectors are not collinear* (i.e., are not parallel or antiparallel). For example, suppose we wish to express the vector **R** shown in Fig. 9-12 as the sum of two vectors, one vector (to be labeled **A**) along the direction designated by I, the other vector (to be labeled **B**) along the direction designated by II. We can do this by drawing a line parallel to direction I through the tail of **R** and a line parallel to direction II through the head of **R**. The intersection of these

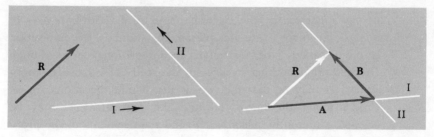

Fig. 9-12   An arbitrary vector **R** *expressed as the sum of two vectors along arbitrary (noncollinear) directions.*

lines provides the point at which the head of **A** meets the tail of **B**. Note that the requirement that the two vectors not be collinear is essential; if directions I and II were parallel or antiparallel, the two lines drawn through the head and tail of **R** would never meet.

The vectors **A** and **B** are called *the components of* **R** *along the directions I and II.* If **R** is a null vector, each of the components vanishes, and vice versa. The process of expressing **R** as the sum of **A** and **B** is called *the decomposition of* **R** *along the directions I and II.* Using this terminology, we can restate the opening proposition of this subsection as follows: Any vector **R** in a plane can always be decomposed along two arbitrary directions, provided only these directions are not parallel or antiparallel; the components are uniquely determined once the directions are specified.

Vector decomposition is of special interest only because it often leads to considerable simplification in problems involving vectors. Decomposition makes it possible to reduce calculations with vectors to calculations with scalars whenever we wish. This is done as follows: Before a problem is attacked, *two standard directions* are chosen, along which *all vectors* encountered in the problem are decomposed. The two directions are almost always chosen *perpendicular to each other.* When the two directions are along the horizontal and the vertical, they are usually referred to as the *x*-direction and the *y*-direction, respectively, a terminology suggested by the Cartesian system of coordinate axes in analytic geometry. (For this reason, the standard decomposition is often called "the Cartesian decomposition," even though Descartes had nothing to do with the study of vector decomposition.) It may be that the two perpendicular directions are *not* chosen along the horizontal and the vertical; they may be oriented differently, according to the requirements of the problem at hand.

Once the two standard directions are chosen, we can find the components of an arbitrary vector **R** by the method described earlier, illustrated in Fig. 9-12. This is illustrated again, for the case of the standard decomposition, in Fig. 9-13(*a*). Alternatively, however, we can also find the components by finding the perpendicular projections of the vector **R** on the two axes, as shown

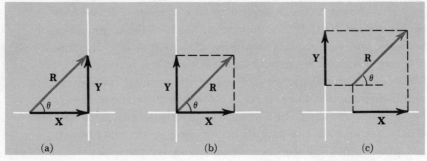

Fig. 9-13   Standard decomposition.

in (*b*) and (*c*) of Fig. 9-13. From this figure it can be seen that the magnitudes X and Y of the two components are given by:

$$X = R \cos \theta$$
$$Y = R \sin \theta \qquad\qquad (9\text{-}3)$$

where θ is the angle between **R** and the *x*-direction. If we now introduce *unit vectors* along the *x* and *y* directions, denoted respectively by $\hat{\imath}$ and $\hat{\jmath}$ (Fig. 9-14), we can express the two components

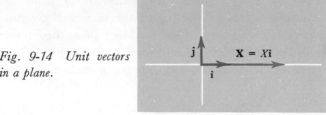

Fig. 9-14   Unit vectors in a plane.

of **R** as follows:

$$\mathbf{X} = X\hat{\imath} = R \cos \theta \, \hat{\imath}$$
$$\mathbf{Y} = Y\hat{\jmath} = R \sin \theta \, \hat{\jmath} \qquad (9\text{-}4)$$

and we can express **R** in terms of its Cartesian components as follows:

$$\mathbf{R} = \mathbf{X} + \mathbf{Y} = X\hat{\imath} + Y\hat{\jmath} = R \cos \theta \, \hat{\imath} + R \sin \theta \, \hat{\jmath} \qquad (9\text{-}5)$$

Conversely, if we are told the *magnitudes* of the two components, we can find the *direction and magnitude* of the *resultant* vector **R** by using the definition of the tangent function and Pythagoras' theorem. In terms of the magnitudes X and Y, the direction θ and the magnitude R of **R** are given by:

$$\tan \theta = Y/X \qquad (9\text{-}6)$$
$$R = \sqrt{X^2 + Y^2} \qquad (9\text{-}7)$$

From Eqs. 9-3, 9-6, and 9-7, we can see the advantage in taking the standard directions to be mutually perpendicular; the simple expressions found in Eqs. 9-3, 9-6, and 9-7 are valid only if **X** is perpendicular to **Y**.

Suppose, now, we wish to find the sum of, say, four vectors in a plane, $\mathbf{R}_1$, $\mathbf{R}_2$, $\mathbf{R}_3$, and $\mathbf{R}_4$, having respective magnitudes R_1, R_2, R_3, and R_4 and making respective angles θ_1, θ_2, θ_3, and θ_4 with the x-axis. We *could* find the sum geometrically by placing the vectors head to tail, or we could try to find the sum analytically by using trigonometric formulas for acute and obtuse triangles; but if we decompose the vectors along two standard directions and *work with the components* along these directions, our task becomes much easier to carry out. By Eq. 9-3, the magnitudes of the various components are given by:

$$X_i = R_i \cos \theta_i \qquad i = 1, 2, 3, 4 \qquad (9\text{-}8)$$
$$Y_i = R_i \sin \theta_i$$

Using the associative law, we find for the sum:

$$\mathbf{R}_1 + \mathbf{R}_2 + \mathbf{R}_3 + \mathbf{R}_4 = \sum_{i=1}^{4} \mathbf{R}_i \equiv \mathbf{R} = (\mathbf{X}_1 + \mathbf{Y}_1)$$
$$+ (\mathbf{X}_2 + \mathbf{Y}_2) + (\mathbf{X}_3 + \mathbf{Y}_3) + (\mathbf{X}_4 + \mathbf{Y}_4)$$
$$= (\mathbf{X}_1 + \mathbf{X}_2 + \mathbf{X}_3 + \mathbf{X}_4) + (\mathbf{Y}_1 + \mathbf{Y}_2 + \mathbf{Y}_3 + \mathbf{Y}_4)$$
$$= \left(\sum_{i=1}^{4} \mathbf{X}_i \right) + \left(\sum_{i=1}^{4} \mathbf{Y}_i \right) \equiv \mathbf{X} + \mathbf{Y} \quad (9\text{-}9)$$

Thus the vector sum **R** has components $\sum_{i=1}^{4} \mathbf{X}_i$ and $\sum_{i=1}^{4} \mathbf{Y}_i$ along the two standard directions. These two components of **R**, however, can be found easily, *because all the* $\mathbf{X}_i$ *are collinear, and all the* $\mathbf{Y}_i$ *are collinear*; this means that the *vector* sum $\sum_{i=1}^{4} \mathbf{X}_i$ has the magnitude of the *scalar* sum $\sum_{i=1}^{4} X_i$, and the direction of $\hat{\mathbf{i}}$, while the vector sum $\sum_{i=1}^{4} \mathbf{Y}_i$ has the magnitude of the scalar sum $\sum_{i=1}^{4} Y_i$ and the direction of $\hat{\mathbf{j}}$. The resultant **R**, therefore, is given by the simple formula:

$$\mathbf{R} = \mathbf{X} + \mathbf{Y} = \left(\sum_{i=1}^{4} X_i \right) \hat{\mathbf{i}} + \left(\sum_{i=1}^{4} Y_i \right) \hat{\mathbf{j}} \qquad (9\text{-}10)$$

and, by Eqs. 9-6 and 9-7, the direction and magnitude of **R** are given by:

$$\tan \theta = \left(\sum_{i=1}^{4} Y_i \right) \Big/ \left(\sum_{i=1}^{4} X_i \right)$$

$$= \left(\sum_{i=1}^{4} R_i \sin \theta_i \right) \Big/ \left(\sum_{i=1}^{4} R_i \cos \theta_i \right)$$

$$R = \sqrt{ \left(\sum_{i=1}^{4} X_i \right)^2 + \left(\sum_{i=1}^{4} Y_i \right)^2 }$$

$$= \sqrt{ \left(\sum_{i=1}^{4} R_i \cos \theta_i \right)^2 + \left(\sum_{i=1}^{4} R_i \sin \theta_i \right)^2 }$$

(9-11)

With the aid of a standard decomposition we can thus calculate sums (and differences) of any number of coplanar vectors, having arbitrary magnitudes and directions, in terms of their components along two standard directions. The result is that all manipulations (the actual mathematical operations of addition and subtraction) are performed with scalar quantities, the magnitudes of the components.

We began by saying that a vector in a plane is fully specified by two quantities—its magnitude and its direction. Alternatively, referring to the standard decomposition, we can say that a vector in a plane is fully specified by two quantities—the magnitudes of its x component and its y component.

6. VECTORS IN THREE DIMENSIONS. THE STANDARD DECOMPOSITION

The results obtained for two dimensions can be extended to three dimensions. In three dimensions, any vector can be expressed as the sum of three components along three arbitrarily chosen directions (any vector can be decomposed along three arbitrary directions) subject to the restriction that the three directions not be such that the components are coplanar.

In three dimensions it is also often convenient to introduce a standard decomposition, for the same reasons as applied in the case of two dimensions: namely, to make certain calculations simpler by reducing operations with vectors to operations with scalars. The three standard directions are chosen to be mutually perpendicular, corresponding to the x, y, z directions in a set of right-handed Cartesian axes. Two alternative ways of finding the components of an arbitrary vector along the standard directions

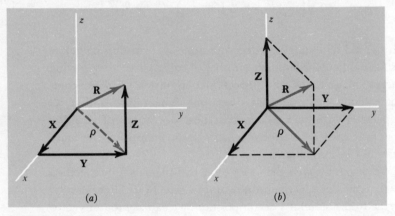

Fig. 9-15 (*a*) $\mathbf{X} + \mathbf{Y} + \mathbf{Z} = \mathbf{R}$ (*b*) *The components shown as*
$(\mathbf{X} + \mathbf{Y} = \rho)$ *projections.*

are shown in Fig. 9-15; the components are, as in the two-dimensional case, the perpendicular projections of the vector $\mathbf{R}$ on the x, y, and z axes, respectively. The projection of $\mathbf{R}$ on the xy-plane is often referred to separately; it is generally labeled ϱ, and is the sum of the $\mathbf{X}$ and $\mathbf{Y}$ components, as can be seen from Fig. 9-15.

In three dimensions we introduce three unit vectors, $\hat{\mathbf{i}}, \hat{\mathbf{j}}, \hat{\mathbf{k}}$, along the x, y, z axes, respectively (Fig. 9-16). In terms of these, we have

$$\left.\begin{array}{l} \mathbf{X} = X\hat{\imath} \\ \mathbf{Y} = Y\hat{\jmath} \\ \mathbf{Z} = Z\hat{k} \end{array}\right\} \qquad (9\text{-}12)$$

$$\mathbf{R} = \mathbf{X} + \mathbf{Y} + \mathbf{Z} = X\hat{\imath} + Y\hat{\jmath} + Z\hat{k} \qquad (9\text{-}13)$$

The magnitude of the resultant **R** can be expressed in terms of

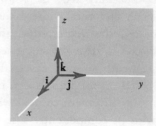

Fig. 9-16 Unit vectors in three dimensions.

the magnitude of the components by successive application of Pythagoras' theorem. Thus (see Fig. 9-15),

$$\begin{array}{l} X^2 + Y^2 = \rho^2 \\ \rho^2 + Z^2 = R^2 \end{array} \qquad (9\text{-}14)$$

Combining these two equations, we find:

$$X^2 + Y^2 + Z^2 = R^2 \qquad (9\text{-}15)$$

To reduce operations with vectors in three dimensions to operations with scalars, we proceed as we did in two dimensions: *All* the vectors appearing in the problem are decomposed along the x, y, z axes, and the three directions are dealt with separately; along each direction separately, all mathematical operations are the same as operations with scalars, since operations with collinear vectors are the same as operations with scalars.

7. TO DECOMPOSE OR NOT TO DECOMPOSE?

The properties of a vector depend only on its direction and magnitude. The properties of a vector in no way depend on the manner in which we choose to decompose it, nor do they depend on whether or not we choose to decompose it. For this reason, it is usually most convenient to deal with vectors directly, without decomposing them, whenever we are talking about the general properties they possess or the laws we expect them to obey. This is especially true of vectors that represent physical quantities (such as forces), where the relation between the mathematical entity, the vector, and the physical entity—for example, the force—is strongly suggested by the picture of a directed line segment; in such cases, the physics and the mathematics are linked in our mind's eye in a very suggestive way, so that it is most convenient to deal with the vector as a whole, rather than with its components. The case has been put with typical force-fulness and clarity by Oliver Heaviside:

> Geometry in the usual Cartesian form, though dealing ultimately with vectors, is not vectorial algebra. It is, in fact, a reduction to scalar algebra by resolution of every vector into three rectangular components, which are manipulated as scalars. Similarly, in the usual treatment of physical vectors [in which they are decomposed], there is an avoidance of the vectors themselves by their resolution into components. That this is a highly artificial process is obvious, but it is often convenient. More often, however, the Cartesian mathematics is ill-adapted to the work it has to do, being lengthy and cumbrous, and frequently calculated to conceal rather than to furnish and exhibit useful results and relations in a ready manner. When we work directly with vectors, we have our attention fixed upon them, and on their mutual relations; and these are usually exhibited in a neat, compact, and expressive form, whose inner meaning is evident at a glance to the practised eye. Put the same formula, however, into the Cartesian form, and—

what a difference! The formula which was expressed by a few letters and symbols in a single line, readable at once, sometimes swells out and covers a whole page! A very close study of the complex array of symbols is then required to find out what it means; and, even though the notation be thoroughly symmetrical, it becomes a work of time and great patience. . . .

Again, in the Cartesian method, we are led away from the physical relations that it is so desirable to bear in mind, to the working out of mathematical exercises upon the components. It becomes, or tends to become, blind mathematics. It was once told as a good joke upon a mathematician that the poor man went mad and mistook his symbols for realities; as M for the moon and S for the sun. There is another side to the story, however. If our object be ultimately physical, rather than mathematical, then the more closely we can identify the symbols with their physical representatives the more usefully can we work, with avoidance of useless—though equally true—mathematical exercises. The mere sight of the arrangement of symbols should call up an immediate picture of the physics symbolised, so that our formulae may become *alive*, as it were. Now this is possible, and indeed, comparatively easy, in vectorial analysis; but is very difficult in Cartesian analysis, beyond a certain point, owing to the geometrically progressive complexity of the expressions to be interpreted and manipulated. Vectorial algebra is the natural language of vectors, and no one who has ever learnt it (not too late in life, however) will ever care to go back from the vitality of vectors to the bulky inanimateness of the Cartesian system.[5]

It is customary and practical to use vector notations and diagrams when dealing with the general behavior of physical entities represented by vectors, and to deal with the standard components of vectors only when making specific calculations, where the decomposition makes the mathematical manipulation more simple to perform.

[5] O. Heaviside, *Electromagnetic Theory* (New York: Dover, 1950), p. 34, paragraph 98.

EXERCISES

1. Given $\mathbf{A} = 3\hat{\imath} + 20\hat{\jmath} - 15\hat{k}$, $\mathbf{B} = 2\hat{\imath} + 5\hat{k}$, $\mathbf{C} = 7\hat{\imath} + 11\hat{\jmath} - 2\hat{k}$, $\mathbf{D} = \hat{\imath} - 4\hat{\jmath} - 7\hat{k}$, calculate: $\mathbf{A} + \mathbf{B}$; $\mathbf{A} + \mathbf{C} - \mathbf{D}$; $\mathbf{A} - \mathbf{B}$; $\mathbf{A} - \mathbf{C} - \mathbf{D}$.

2. Given $\mathbf{A}$ and $\mathbf{B}$, we know how to find $\mathbf{A} + \mathbf{B}$ and $\mathbf{A} - \mathbf{B}$. Suppose we are given the vectors $\mathbf{A} + \mathbf{B}$ and $\mathbf{A} - \mathbf{B}$; how could we find $\mathbf{A}$ and $\mathbf{B}$ from these?

3. Prove that vector addition is associative.

4. Show that the two methods described in the text for the addition of three vectors give the same resultant sum.

5. Vectors are drawn from the center of a regular pentagon to all the vertices. Show that the sum of these vectors is zero.

6. Suppose the equations $m\mathbf{A} + n\mathbf{B} = 0$ and $m + n = 0$ are both satisfied. Show that $\mathbf{A}$ and $\mathbf{B}$ are equal in magnitude and direction.

7. Suppose that three numbers l, m, n exist (none of them equal to zero) such that $l\mathbf{A} + m\mathbf{B} + n\mathbf{C} = 0$. Show that $\mathbf{A}$, $\mathbf{B}$, and $\mathbf{C}$ are parallel to one plane.

8. Given three coplanar vectors of magnitudes 3, 4, and 5, respectively, under what conditions will their sum vanish?

9. Find the x and y components of a unit vector lying in the x, y plane and making an angle of $\pi/4$ rad with the x-axis.

10. An x, y coordinate system is transformed into an x', y' coordinate system by rotation through an angle θ. Find the x and y components of the new unit vectors $\hat{\imath}'$ and $\hat{\jmath}'$; using these, express $\hat{\imath}'$ and $\hat{\jmath}'$ in terms of $\hat{\imath}$ and $\hat{\jmath}$.

11. Show that the vectors $\mathbf{A} = A \cos\theta\,\hat{\imath} + A \sin\theta\,\hat{\jmath}$ and $\mathbf{B} = B \cos\theta\,\hat{\imath} + B \sin\theta\,\hat{\jmath}$ are parallel.

12. If $\mathbf{A}$ and $\mathbf{B}$ are two vectors drawn from the origin to the points A, B, respectively, find (in terms of $\mathbf{A}$ and $\mathbf{B}$) the vector drawn from the origin to the midpoint of the line joining A and B.

13. Given the vectors $\mathbf{A} = \hat{\imath} + \hat{\jmath} - \hat{k}$ and $\mathbf{B} = 3\hat{\imath} - 2\hat{\jmath} - \hat{k}$, drawn from the origin, show that the vector from the head of $\mathbf{A}$ to the head of $\mathbf{B}$ is parallel to the x, y plane and find its magnitude.

14. The following four vectors are drawn from the origin: $\mathbf{A} = \hat{\imath} + \hat{\jmath} + \hat{k}$; $\mathbf{B} = 2\hat{\imath} + 3\hat{\jmath}$; $\mathbf{C} = 3\hat{\imath} + 5\hat{\jmath} - 2\hat{k}$; $\mathbf{D} = \hat{k} - \hat{\jmath}$. Show that the vector drawn from the head of $\mathbf{A}$ to the head of $\mathbf{B}$ is parallel to the vector drawn from the head of $\mathbf{D}$ to the head of $\mathbf{C}$. Find the ratio of the lengths of these two vectors.

15. Oliver Heaviside once wrote the following:

It is worth while to point out that by means of the addition property of vectors a good deal of geometry can be simply done— better than by Euclid, a considerable part of whose 12 books consists of examples of how not to do it (especially Book V.). There is a Society for the Improvement of Geometrical Teaching. I have no knowledge of its work; but as to the need of improvement there can be no question whilst the reign of Euclid continues. My own idea of a useful course is to begin with arithmetic, and then, not Euclid, but algebra. Next, not Euclid, but practical geometry, solid as well as plane; not demonstrations, but to make acquaintance. Then, not Euclid, but elementary vectors, conjoined with algebra, and applied to geometry. Addition first; then the scalar product. This covers a large ground. When more advanced, bring in the vector product. Elementary calculus should go on simultaneously, and come into the vector algebraic geometry after a bit. Euclid might be an extra course for learned men, like Homer. But Euclid for children is barbarous.[6]

Using what you have learned about vectors, prove that: (a) the diagonals of a parallelogram bisect each other; (b) the line joining the midpoints of the two sides of a triangle is parallel to the third side. Compare your proof with the Euclidean proof (to be found in any standard text book of Euclidean geometry).

[6] Heaviside, *Electromagnetic Theory*, p. 38, Paragraph 106.

10

PRODUCTS OF VECTORS

1. THE SCALAR PRODUCT

For the solution of many physical problems involving vectors it turns out to be convenient to introduce two kinds of products of a pair of vectors. One kind, called the *scalar product*, takes two vectors and defines a *scalar* in terms of them. The second kind, called a *vector product*, takes two vectors and defines a *vector* in terms of them.

The scalar product of two vectors **A** and **B** is written **A · B**, and is defined as the scalar which is the product of the magnitudes of **A** and **B** and of the cosine of the angle between them, as specified in Fig. 10-1.

$$\mathbf{A} \cdot \mathbf{B} \equiv AB \cos \theta \tag{10-1}$$

Scalar multiplication of two vectors is commutative, since the cosine of the angle from B to $A = \cos(-\theta) = \cos \theta$.

Fig. 10-1   Quantities involved in the definition of a scalar product.

The usefulness of the scalar product stems essentially from its geometrical significance. As can be seen from Fig. 10-2, $A \cos \theta$ is the magnitude of the *perpendicular projection of* **A** *on* **B**, and $B \cos \theta$ is the magnitude of the perpendicular projection of **B** on **A**. The scalar product of two vectors, as defined in Definition 10-1, is thus seen to be the product of the magnitude of one vector times the magnitude of the *projection* of the other vector on the first. Scalar multiplication, in other words, finds use when we wish to "pick out" the component of one vector along another.

In general, the presence of the cosine function in the Definition 10-1 indicates that the scalar product will come into play when we are dealing with projections of any type. For example, consider a finite plane area of area S (in arbitrary square units). This area can be represented by a vector, since it is specified by a magnitude (the magnitude of the area, S) and by a direction (the orientation of the plane area in space). The direction is uniquely specified most simply by giving the direction of a single line, the *perpendicular* to the plane (since we know from elementary geometry that all planes drawn perpendicular to a given line

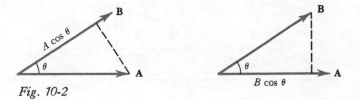

Fig. 10-2

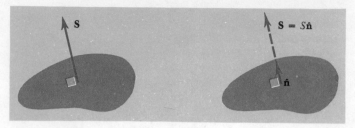

Fig. 10-3   Representation of a plane area by a vector.

have the same orientation). Thus, in summary, we can represent the plane area by a single vector **S**, whose magnitude is S and whose direction is perpendicular to the plane area; or, introducing a unit vector $\hat{n}$ perpendicular to the area, the plane area can be represented by a single vector $S\hat{n}$ (Fig. 10-3).

Now, suppose we want to find the projection of the plane area S on another plane, oriented differently from **S**—for example, suppose we want to find the projection of S on a plane F oriented perpendicular to the unit vector $\hat{\epsilon}$ (Fig. 10-4). If we call the area of projection S', we see that

$$S' = S \cos \theta \tag{10-2}$$

where θ is the angle between the plane of S and the plane F. However, the angle between the planes is the same as the angle between the unit vectors perpendicular to the planes, $\hat{n}$ and $\hat{\epsilon}$.

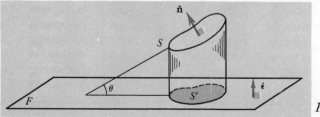

Fig. 10-4

By the definition of the scalar product,

$$\hat{n} \cdot \hat{\varepsilon} = |\hat{n}| \, |\hat{\varepsilon}| \cos \theta = \cos \theta \qquad (10\text{-}3)$$

since $|\hat{n}| = |\hat{\varepsilon}| = 1$, by definition. We therefore have, by Eqs. 10-2 and 10-3,

$$S' = S\hat{n} \cdot \hat{\varepsilon} = (S\hat{n}) \cdot \hat{\varepsilon} = \mathbf{S} \cdot \hat{\varepsilon} \qquad (10\text{-}4)$$

The projection of one plane area, represented by the vector $\mathbf{S} = S\hat{n}$, on another plane, whose orientation is represented by $\hat{\varepsilon}$, is thus given by the scalar product of the two vectors. Again, we see that the scalar product comes into play where projections are involved.

If the geometric interpretation of a scalar product is invoked, it is not difficult to prove the *distributive law* for the scalar product of vectors:

$$\mathbf{A} \cdot (\mathbf{B} + \mathbf{C}) = \mathbf{A} \cdot \mathbf{B} + \mathbf{A} \cdot \mathbf{C} \qquad (10\text{-}5)$$

From the definition and geometric interpretation of the scalar product, we see that when two vectors are parallel ($\theta = 0$, $\cos \theta = 1$), the scalar product is just the product of the magnitudes of the two vectors; and when the two vectors are mutually perpendicular ($\theta - \pi/2$, $\cos \theta = 0$), the scalar product vanishes—as is to be expected, since the projection of a vector on a direction perpendicular to it vanishes:

$$\begin{aligned} \mathbf{A} \cdot \mathbf{B} &= AB \qquad (A \parallel B) \\ \mathbf{A} \cdot \mathbf{B} &= 0 \qquad (A \perp B) \end{aligned} \qquad (10\text{-}6)$$

It is relatively simple to find a multiplication table for the standard Cartesian unit vectors $\hat{\imath}$, $\hat{\jmath}$, $\hat{k}$.[1] The products of the unit vectors are: $\hat{\imath} \cdot \hat{\imath} = i^2 = 1 = \hat{\jmath} \cdot \hat{\jmath} = \hat{k} \cdot \hat{k}$, while $\hat{\imath} \cdot \hat{\jmath} = \hat{\jmath} \cdot \hat{k} = \hat{k} \cdot \hat{\imath} = 0$, by Eq. 10-6. Table form is given in Table 10-1.

---

[1] All expressions given for three dimensions can be applied to two dimensions by dropping the third unit vector $\hat{k}$.

Table 10-1 Scalar Products
of Unit Vectors

	$\hat{\imath}$	$\hat{\jmath}$	$\hat{k}$
$\hat{\imath}$	1	0	0
$\hat{\jmath}$	0	1	0
$\hat{k}$	0	0	1

Using the multiplication table, we can find an expression for the scalar product $\mathbf{A} \cdot \mathbf{B}$ in terms of the standard x, y, z components of the vectors $\mathbf{A}$ and $\mathbf{B}$. If we label components as follows:

$$\mathbf{A} = \mathbf{A}_x + \mathbf{A}_y + \mathbf{A}_z = A_x\hat{\imath} + A_y\hat{\jmath} + A_z\hat{k}$$
$$\mathbf{B} = \mathbf{B}_x + \mathbf{B}_y + \mathbf{B}_z = B_x\hat{\imath} + B_y\hat{\jmath} + B_z\hat{k} \tag{10-7}$$

then, using the multiplication table and the distributive law, we find as an alternative expression to Definition 10-1 for the scalar product the following:

$$\mathbf{A} \cdot \mathbf{B} = A_xB_x + A_yB_y + A_zB_z \tag{10-8}$$

(The reader should verify this.) In the particular case of the product $\mathbf{A} \cdot \mathbf{A}$, we have:

$$\mathbf{A} \cdot \mathbf{A} = A_x{}^2 + A_y{}^2 + A_z{}^2 = A^2 \tag{10-9}$$

2. THE VECTOR PRODUCT

The vector product of two vectors $\mathbf{A}$ and $\mathbf{B}$ is written $\mathbf{A} \times \mathbf{B}$ and is defined to be the vector whose magnitude is the product of the magnitudes of $\mathbf{A}$ and $\mathbf{B}$ and of the sine of the angle between them, and whose direction is perpendicular to $\mathbf{A}$ and $\mathbf{B}$ such that $\mathbf{A}$, $\mathbf{B}$, and $\mathbf{A} \times \mathbf{B}$ are a right-handed triplet.[2]

$$|\mathbf{A} \times \mathbf{B}| = AB \sin \theta \tag{10-10}$$

[2] That is, $\mathbf{A}$, $\mathbf{B}$, $\mathbf{A} \times \mathbf{B}$ lie along the extended thumb, index, and middle fingers of the right hand, respectively. See Chapter 3, Section 9.

A number of important features of the vector product can be seen immediately from its definition. First, the vector **A × B** cannot be expressed as a sum of vectors along **A** and **B** (i.e., cannot be expressed in terms of any "linear combination" of **A** and **B**, $a\mathbf{A} + b\mathbf{B}$, regardless of the values assigned the numbers a and b): This is because **A × B** is *perpendicular* to the plane determined by **A** and **B**, while, as we have seen, all sums of vectors along **A** and **B** give vectors that lie *in* the plane determined by **A** and **B**.[3]

Second, *vector multiplication is not commutative*. The product depends on the order of the factors. The *magnitude* of **A × B**, as given in Eq. 10-10, is, to be sure, independent of the order of the factors, but the *direction* of **A × B** depends on the order, since the direction is defined to be perpendicular to **A** and **B** such that **A**, **B** and **A × B** form a right-handed set. If we reverse the order of the factors, and consider **B × A**, the definition then tells us that the direction of **B × A** is perpendicular to **B** and **A**, but in such a way that **B**, **A** and **B × A** form a right-handed set. This means that **B × A** must be in the direction opposite to **A × B** (see Fig. 10-5), so that

$$\mathbf{B \times A} = -\mathbf{A \times B}$$ (B × A and A × B have equal magnitudes but opposite directions)   (10-11)

[3] This is expressed by saying that vector **A × B** is independent of the vectors **A** and **B**.

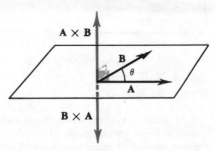

Fig. 10-5 The vector products **A × B** *and* **B × A**.

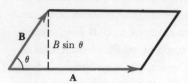

Fig. 10-6 Parallelogram formed by **A**, **B** *viewed from above.*

Equation 10-11 tells us that vector multiplication is noncommutative. Any kind of multiplication for which reversal of the factors gives different results is called noncommutative multiplication; the particularly simple example of vector multiplication, where reversal of the factors gives a result that differs only in *sign*, is called *anticommutative*.[4]

The vector product, like the scalar product, can be interpreted geometrically, although this by no means exhausts the area of its usefulness in science. Consider the plane parallelogram defined by the sides **A** and **B** (see Fig. 10-6). The *area* of this parallelogram, in square units, is given by the product of the length of the base and the length of the height, which, from the figure, can be seen to be $AB \sin \theta$. Thus, the *magnitude* of the vector product **A** ✕ **B** is just the area of the plane parallelogram

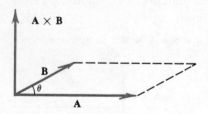

Fig. 10-7 Perspective view of **A, B,** *and* **A ✕ B,** *and of the geometric meaning of* **A ✕ B**.

[4] For many readers this is the first example of noncommutative multiplication to be encountered, although those who have studied advanced algebra know that matrix multiplication is also noncommutative (and not even anticommutative).

formed by **A** and **B**. The *direction* of the vector product is perpendicular to the plane of the parallelogram (i.e., in the direction normal to the plane) which, as we have seen in Section 1, is the *direction* of the vector that represents the plane area involved (Fig. 10-7). Thus, the vector product **A** × **B**, because of the particular way we have defined its magnitude and direction, is just the vector that represents the area of the plane parallelogram formed by **A** and **B**.

Referring to the geometric interpretation of the vector product, it is not difficult to show that vector multiplication obeys the distributive law:

$$\mathbf{A} \times (\mathbf{B} + \mathbf{C}) = \mathbf{A} \times \mathbf{B} + \mathbf{A} \times \mathbf{C} \qquad (10\text{-}12)$$

From either the definition preceding Eq. 10-10 or the geometrical interpretation, we can see that the vector product of two collinear vectors (which includes, as a special case, the vector product **A** × **A** of a vector with itself) is a null vector ($\theta = 0$ or π, $\sin \theta = 0$, and the parallelogram degenerates into a zero-area line); while the magnitude of the vector product of two perpendicular vectors is just the product of the magnitudes ($\theta = \pi/2$, $\sin \theta = 1$, and the parallelogram becomes a rectangle whose area is just the product of the magnitudes of the sides)

$$\begin{aligned} \mathbf{A} \times \mathbf{B} &= 0 & &(\mathbf{A} \parallel \mathbf{B} \text{ or } \mathbf{A} \text{ anti-} \parallel \mathbf{B}) \\ |\mathbf{A} \times \mathbf{B}| &= AB & &(\mathbf{A} \perp \mathbf{B}) \end{aligned} \qquad (10\text{-}13)$$

A multiplication table for vector products of the $\hat{\imath}$, $\hat{\jmath}$, $\hat{k}$ unit vectors taken two at a time can be prepared. By Eq. 10-13 we see that $\hat{\imath} \times \hat{\imath} = \hat{\jmath} \times \hat{\jmath} = \hat{k} \times \hat{k} = 0$. To find $\hat{\imath} \times \hat{\jmath}$, we note that by Eq. 10-13 its magnitude is 1, and its direction is perpendicular to $\hat{\imath}$ and $\hat{\jmath}$ such that it forms a right-handed triplet with $\hat{\imath}$ and $\hat{\jmath}$: Thus, it is along the z-axis, and has unit magnitude; or, in other words, it is $\hat{k}$. By Eq. 10-11, we see that $\hat{\jmath} \times \hat{\imath} = -\hat{k}$. In similar manner, we can complete the table as shown in Table 10-2.

*Table 10-2   Vector Products
of Unit Vectors*

	$\hat{\imath}$	$\hat{\jmath}$	$\hat{k}$
$\hat{\imath}$	0	$\hat{k}$	$-\hat{\jmath}$
$\hat{\jmath}$	$-\hat{k}$	0	$\hat{\imath}$
$\hat{k}$	$\hat{\jmath}$	$-\hat{\imath}$	0

The following is a simple way to remember the sign for any entry in the above table: *cyclic* permutations of the triplet (i,j,k) are permutations changing the leading member of the triplet but not its order, viz. (j,k,i) and (k,i,j). All products in which the factors are cyclic permutations of (i,j,k) have a positive sign: $\hat{\imath} \times \hat{\jmath} = \hat{k}$, $\hat{\jmath} \times \hat{k} = \hat{\imath}$, $\hat{k} \times \hat{\imath} = \hat{\jmath}$; all other products are negative.

Using this multiplication table and the distributive law, we can express the vector product of two vectors **A** and **B** in terms of the components of **A** and **B** given by Eq. 10-7. The result is:

$$\begin{aligned}
\mathbf{A} \times \mathbf{B} &= (A_x\hat{\imath} + A_y\hat{\jmath} + A_z\hat{k}) \times (B_x\hat{\imath} + B_y\hat{\jmath} + B_z\hat{k}) \\
&= (A_yB_z - A_zB_y)\hat{\imath} + (A_zB_x - A_xB_z)\hat{\jmath} \qquad (10\text{-}14) \\
&\quad + (A_xB_y - A_yB_x)\hat{k}
\end{aligned}$$

(The reader should verify this.)

3. TRIPLE PRODUCTS

Two types of triple products (products involving three vectors as factors) recur in various calculations: the scalar triple product and the vector triple product.

1. *The scalar triple product:* This is the product $\mathbf{A} \cdot (\mathbf{B} \times \mathbf{C})$, the scalar product of **A** and a vector which itself is the vector

product **B** ✕ **C**. Since it is nonsense to write (**A** · **B**) ✕ **C**, we can drop the parentheses. From Eqs. 10-8 and 10-14 (the expressions for the scalar and vector products in terms of Cartesian components), we find the following expression for the scalar triple product in terms of the components:

$$\mathbf{A} \cdot \mathbf{B} \times \mathbf{C} = A_x(B_yC_z - B_zC_y) + A_y(B_zC_x - B_xC_z)$$
$$+ A_z(B_xC_y - B_yC_x) \quad (10\text{-}15)$$

From the right-hand side of Eq. 10-15 we see that making cyclic permutations of the letters (*ABC*) (for example, replacing *A* by *B*, *B* by *C*, and *C* by *A*) leaves the value of the triple product *unaltered;* hence, this must be true of the left-hand side too, so that:

$$\mathbf{A} \cdot \mathbf{B} \times \mathbf{C} = \mathbf{B} \cdot \mathbf{C} \times \mathbf{A} = \mathbf{C} \cdot \mathbf{A} \times \mathbf{B} \quad (10\text{-}16)[5]$$

Any other permutation leads to a change in sign. For example:

$$\mathbf{B} \cdot \mathbf{A} \times \mathbf{C} = -\mathbf{A} \cdot \mathbf{B} \times \mathbf{C} \quad (10\text{-}17)$$

The scalar triple product has a simple geometric interpretation. The vectors **A**, **B**, **C** form the sides of a parallelepiped (Fig. 10-8). **B** ✕ **C** is the vector representing the area of the

[5] Equations 10-16 show that the scalar triple product is not affected by interchanging the dot and the cross.

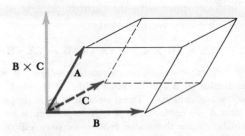

Fig. 10-8 Geometric interpretation of the scalar triple product.

parallelogram formed by **B** and **C**: its magnitude is this area, and it is perpendicular to the plane of the parallelogram. The scalar product **A** · (**B** × **C**) is the projection of **A** on the perpendicular to the plane of B and C (i.e., the height of the parallelepiped) times the area of the base parallelogram; in other words, **A** · (**B** × **C**) is the *volume* of the parallelepiped. From this, or from the definition directly, it can be seen that the scalar triple product vanishes if any two factors are collinear, since then the parallelepiped degenerates into a plane area of zero volume.[6]

2. *The vector triple product:* This is the product **A** × (**B** × **C**) and is a vector. The question is: Which vector is it, and how can this vector be expressed simply? The vector (**B** × **C**) is perpendicular to the plane of **B** and **C**. The vector **A** × (**B** × **C**) is perpendicular in turn to the vector **B** × **C**, and hence is *in* the plane of **B** and **C**. (We assume **B** and **C** are not collinear.) By the discussion of Chapter 9, Section 5, since **A** × (**B** × **C**) is in the plane of **B** and **C**, it can be expressed as the sum of two vectors, along the directions of **B** and **C**, respectively:

$$\mathbf{A} \times (\mathbf{B} \times \mathbf{C}) = b\mathbf{B} + c\mathbf{C} \tag{10-18}$$

where b and c are still to be determined. Applying Eq. 10-14 twice, once to (**B** × **C**) and again to **A** × (**B** × **C**), we can express the left-hand side of Eq. 10-18 in terms of components and compare with the right-hand side in terms of components. In this way we find that:

$$\mathbf{A} \times (\mathbf{B} \times \mathbf{C}) = (\mathbf{A} \cdot \mathbf{C})\mathbf{B} - (\mathbf{A} \cdot \mathbf{B})\mathbf{C} \tag{10-19}[7]$$

[6] Another way of seeing this is as follows: **B** × **C** is, by definition, perpendicular to **B** and **C**, and vanishes if **B** and **C** are collinear. Suppose **B** and **A** are collinear. Then, since **B** × **C** is perpendicular to **B**, and since **B** and **A** are collinear, **B** × **C** is perpendicular to **A** too; hence, **A** · **B** × **C** vanishes, since the scalar product of perpendicular vectors vanishes. The same holds if **C** and **A** are collinear. Thus, the scalar triple product vanishes if any two factors are collinear, Q.E.D.

[7] By taking the scalar product of **A** with the left-hand side and right-

Using the anticommutative property of the vector product, we have:

$$(\mathbf{B} \times \mathbf{C}) \times \mathbf{A} = (\mathbf{A} \cdot \mathbf{B})\mathbf{C} - (\mathbf{A} \cdot \mathbf{C})\mathbf{B} \qquad (10\text{-}20)$$

Note that the place of the parentheses is crucial. $\mathbf{A} \times (\mathbf{B} \times \mathbf{C})$ and $(\mathbf{A} \times \mathbf{B}) \times \mathbf{C}$ are two very different entities!

EXERCISES

1. Given $\mathbf{A} = 3\hat{\imath} + 20\hat{\jmath} - 15\hat{k}$, $\mathbf{B} = 2\hat{\imath} + 5\hat{k}$, $\mathbf{C} = 7\hat{\imath} + 11\hat{\jmath} - 2\hat{k}$, calculate: $\mathbf{A} \cdot \mathbf{B}$; $\mathbf{A} \cdot \mathbf{A} = A^2$; $\mathbf{A} \times \mathbf{B}$; $\mathbf{A} \cdot \mathbf{C} - \mathbf{B} \cdot \mathbf{C}$; $\mathbf{A} \times \mathbf{B} + \mathbf{B} \times \mathbf{A}$; $\mathbf{A} \times \mathbf{C} - \mathbf{C} \times \mathbf{B}$; $\mathbf{A} \cdot (\mathbf{B} \times \mathbf{C})$. Show that $\mathbf{A} \times \mathbf{B}$ is perpendicular to $\mathbf{A}$ and to $\mathbf{B}$. Find the sine and cosine of the angle between $\mathbf{A}$ and $\mathbf{B}$.
2. Given $\mathbf{A} = \cos \theta \, \hat{\imath} + \sin \theta \, \hat{\jmath}$, $\mathbf{B} = \cos \phi \, \hat{\imath} + \sin \phi \, \hat{\jmath}$, $\mathbf{C} = \cos \phi \, \hat{\imath} - \sin \phi \, \hat{\jmath}$, find the scalar and vector products of these vectors taken in pairs. (Simplify the expressions you obtain with the aid of the trigonometric formulas given in Chapter 4, Section 4.)
3. Given $\mathbf{A} = 2\hat{\imath} - 3\hat{\jmath}$, $\mathbf{B} = 3\hat{\imath} + 4\hat{\jmath}$, find the component of $\mathbf{A}$ along $\mathbf{B}$ graphically and by calculation.
4. Given $\mathbf{A} = 2\hat{\imath} + 4\hat{\jmath} - 7\hat{k}$, $\mathbf{B} = 2\hat{\imath} + 6\hat{\jmath} + x\hat{k}$, what value of x will make $\mathbf{A} \perp \mathbf{B}$?
5. Prove Eq. 10-5, with the aid of the geometric interpretation of a scalar product.
6. Prove Eq. 10-12, with the aid of the geometric interpretation of a vector product.

---

hand side of Eq. 10-18 we find that:

$$0 = b(\mathbf{A} \cdot \mathbf{B}) + c(\mathbf{A} \cdot \mathbf{C})$$

since $\mathbf{A} \cdot \mathbf{A} \times (\mathbf{B} \times \mathbf{C})$ vanishes, it being a scalar triple product with two factors identical. Thus, we find:

$$b/c = -(\mathbf{A} \cdot \mathbf{C})/(\mathbf{A} \cdot \mathbf{B})$$

as is evident from Eq. 10-19. But this gives only the ratio b/c, and does not tell us what b and c are individually. To find b and c, the detailed calculation must be carried out.

7. Show in detail that Eq. 10-19 is valid.
8. Prove that the diagonals of a rhombus are mutually perpendicular.
9. Show that $\mathbf{A} \times (\mathbf{B} \times \mathbf{C}) + \mathbf{B} \times (\mathbf{C} \times \mathbf{A}) + \mathbf{C} \times (\mathbf{B} \times \mathbf{A}) = 0$.
10. Show that $(\mathbf{A} \times \mathbf{B}) \cdot (\mathbf{C} \times \mathbf{D}) = (\mathbf{A} \cdot \mathbf{C})(\mathbf{B} \cdot \mathbf{D}) - (\mathbf{A} \cdot \mathbf{D})(\mathbf{B} \cdot \mathbf{C})$.
11. Given an arbitrary vector $\mathbf{A}$ and an arbitrary unit vector $\hat{n}$, prove that $\mathbf{A} = (\mathbf{A} \cdot \hat{n})\hat{n} + \hat{n} \times (\mathbf{A} \times \hat{n})$. (This formula represents the decomposition of $\mathbf{A}$ into two components, one parallel and one perpendicular to $\hat{n}$.)

11

THE DERIVATIVE
OF A VECTOR

A vector is defined by a magnitude *and* a direction. We have seen
in Chapter 9 that the two aspects of a vector **V** can be separated
if we introduce the unit vector $\hat{\mathbf{v}}$ in the direction of **V**, in terms
of which we can write:

$$\mathbf{V} = V\hat{\mathbf{v}} \tag{11-1}$$

where V is the magnitude of **V**. A vector can therefore change
in one of three ways: (1) the *magnitude* alone can change, with
the direction remaining constant (i.e., the vector can stretch or
shrink, while pointing in the same direction); (2) the *direction*
alone can change, with the magnitude remaining constant (i.e.,
the vector can change orientation, while maintaining fixed
length); (3) both magnitude and direction can change (i.e., the

vector can change its size *and* orientation). We shall treat each possibility separately.

As long as a vector's direction remains fixed, and only the magnitude is allowed to change, the problem in no way differs from any other case where a scalar variable undergoes change. The magnitude, in other words, is simply a scalar function, which is what we have been discussing exclusively up till this section. Therefore, in case (1), we can write for the infinitesimal change $d\mathbf{V}$ of a vector whose direction remains fixed (see Fig. 11-1):

$$d\mathbf{V} = (dV)\hat{\mathbf{v}} \qquad (\hat{\mathbf{v}} \text{ fixed}) \tag{11-2}$$

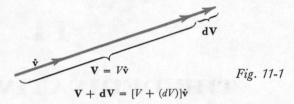

$$\mathbf{V} = V\hat{\mathbf{v}}$$
Fig. 11-1
$$\mathbf{V} + d\mathbf{V} = [V + (dV)]\hat{\mathbf{v}}$$

In the second case, we are interested in finding $d\mathbf{V}$ when the vector, with V constant, changes direction by an infinitesimal angle $d\theta$. Since V is fixed, all we need to find is $d\hat{\mathbf{v}}$:

$$d\mathbf{V} = V d\hat{\mathbf{v}} \qquad (V \text{ fixed}) \tag{11-3}$$

i.e., all we need to find is the change in the unit vector $\hat{\mathbf{v}}$ when it changes direction by an infinitesimal angle $d\theta$. To find this, we will examine the finite change $\Delta\hat{\mathbf{v}}$ resulting from rotation through a finite angle $\Delta\theta$, and take the limit $\Delta\theta \rightarrow 0$.

Figure 11-2 shows the situation for finite angle $\Delta\theta$. $\hat{\mathbf{v}}$ is the unit vector before change of direction, $\hat{\mathbf{v}} + \Delta\hat{\mathbf{v}}$ is the unit vector after

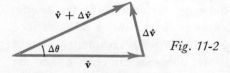

Fig. 11-2

change of direction by angle $\Delta\theta$. $\hat{v} + \Delta\hat{v}$ has unit magnitude too, of course, since it is still a unit vector; but it differs from $\hat{v}$ because it points in a different direction from $\hat{v}$. Using the usual rules of vector addition, we can find the vector that is the difference between $\hat{v} + \Delta\hat{v}$ and $\hat{v}$; this is shown in the figure as the vector $\Delta\hat{v}$. Note that $\hat{v}$, $\hat{v} + \Delta\hat{v}$, and $\Delta\hat{v}$ form an isosceles triangle with apex angle $\Delta\theta$.

The figure deserves study, as it points up the difference between vectors and scalars. In the figure we are dealing with the change of an entity whose *magnitude* remains fixed; it becomes no bigger or smaller than it was before. All that happens is that its *direction* changes, but this is no less a *real* change for vectors than is a change in magnitude; change in direction, too, leads to actual change in the entity, as shown by the difference vector $\Delta\hat{v}$ that measures this change.

We can now pass to the limit $\Delta\theta \rightarrow 0$. In the limit, Fig. 11-2 comes to look more like Fig. 11-3 (to the extent that infinitesimals

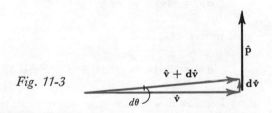

Fig. 11-3

can be pictured in finite-sized diagrams). We see that in the limit, as the apex angle $\rightarrow 0$, *the base* $d\hat{v}$ *becomes perpendicular to the sides.* Furthermore, in the limit, the isosceles triangle becomes indistinguishable from an infinitesimal segment (having apex angle $d\theta$) of a unit circle, since the base of such a segment is also straight when the apex angle is infinitesimal (see Chapter 6, Section 7, where we found the limit of $\sin \theta/\theta$). This tells us that the *magnitude* of $d\hat{v}$ is equal to $d\theta$ (in radians), since $d\theta$ is the ratio of the magnitude of the intercepted arc (here, $|d\hat{v}|$) to the magnitude of the radius (here, $|\hat{\mathbf{v}}| = 1$, by definition). Thus,

$$|d\hat{\mathbf{v}}| = d\theta \qquad (11\text{-}4)$$

Introducing the unit vector $\hat{\mathbf{p}}$ perpendicular to $\hat{\mathbf{v}}$ (and hence to **V**) as shown in Figs. 11-3 and 11-4, we have, in terms of the

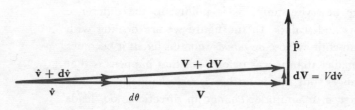

Fig. 11-4

magnitude and direction of $d\hat{\mathbf{v}}$:

$$d\hat{\mathbf{v}} = |d\hat{\mathbf{v}}|\,\hat{\mathbf{p}} = d\theta\,\hat{\mathbf{p}} \qquad (11\text{-}5)$$

and, by Eq. 11-3:

$$d\mathbf{V} = V\,d\hat{\mathbf{v}} = (V\,d\theta)\hat{\mathbf{p}} \qquad (V \text{ fixed}) \qquad (11\text{-}6)$$

Turning now to the case where both magnitude and direction change, we have—adding the two effects, Eqs. 11-3 and 11-6—as a generally valid expression:

$$d\mathbf{V} = (dV)\hat{\mathbf{v}} + (V\,d\theta)\hat{\mathbf{p}} \qquad \text{for } \mathbf{V} = V\hat{\mathbf{v}} \qquad (11\text{-}7)$$

Thus, the most general possible infinitesimal change a vector can undergo has two components: one in the direction of the original vector, arising from the change in magnitude of the vector, and a second in a direction perpendicular to the original vector, arising from the change in direction of the vector.

EXERCISES

1. Consider the vector $\mathbf{r} = A(\cos \omega t \,\hat{\imath} + \sin \omega t \,\hat{\jmath})$, where A and ω are constants. Find: $|\mathbf{r}|$; $d\mathbf{r}/dt$; $|d\mathbf{r}/dt|$; $d^2\mathbf{r}/dt^2$; $(d\mathbf{r}/dt) \cdot (d^2\mathbf{r}/dt^2)$; $\mathbf{r} \times (d^2\mathbf{r}/dt^2)$.

2. Show that if $\mathbf{r} \cdot d\mathbf{r} = 0$, the magnitude of $\mathbf{r}$ is constant; and that if $\mathbf{r} \times d\mathbf{r} = 0$, the direction of $\mathbf{r}$ is constant. (Thus, for $\mathbf{r}$ to be constant, $\mathbf{r} \cdot d\mathbf{r} = 0$ and $\mathbf{r} \times d\mathbf{r} = 0$ must both hold. Another way of saying this is that $\mathbf{r} \cdot d\mathbf{r} = 0$ and $\mathbf{r} \times d\mathbf{r} = 0$ implies $d\mathbf{r} = 0$.)

3. Prove Eq. 11-7 by applying the rule for differentiating a product to the product $\mathbf{V} = V\hat{\mathbf{v}}$.

ANSWERS TO
THE EXERCISES

CHAPTER 1

1. No. $\triangle ABD \sim \triangle BCD \sim \triangle ACB$. **2.** No. No. No. No. **3.** All have corresponding angles equal (45°, 45°, 90°). No. **4.** No. **5.** 60°, 45°, 30°, 26°, 12°. **6.** Yes. (This is the famous triangle inequality.) **7.** 2 ft. **8.** From the edge that has been cut, which is longer than the ends that have been joined. **9.** Circle in the square. Square's perimeter: circle's perimeter $= 4:\pi$. Square's area: circle's area $= 4:\pi$. This is a very special case where the ratio of perimeters is the same as the ratio of areas. **10.** $d^2/2$. **11.** Doubled. Tripled. **12.** By a factor of 4. The area is increased by a factor of 9. **13.** By a factor of 4. By a factor of 8. By factors of 9 and 27, respectively. **14.** 7.

CHAPTER 2

1. $x^2 - x - 6$; $x^3 - x^2 - 26x + 20$; $x^2 - 169$;
$x^4 + 3x^3 - 11x^2 - 27x + 18$. **2.** $x(3x + 5)$; $2(2x^3 - x + 3)$;
$x(4x^2 - 3x + 6)$; $4x(3x^2 - 1)$; $(x + 4)(x - 4)$; $(x + 4)(x + 4)$.
3. $(a^{\frac{1}{3}} - b^{\frac{1}{3}})(a^{\frac{1}{3}} + b^{\frac{1}{3}})$. **4.** First, second, fourth. **5.** $a = 4$;
$(2x + 1)(2x + 1) = 0$. **6.** 8 cm. **7.** 15. **8.** 68 yr old. **9.** 10.
10. 3602 miles. **11.** $A = wl$. $A = f(w) = g(l)$. $A = 3w^2 = l^2/3$.
12. $h^2 = a^2 + b^2$. $h^2 = 2a^2$. **14.** $-x^3/3$. **15.** $x + a - 3$; $x^2 + 2ax + a^2$;
$2x^2 + 4ax + 2a^2 + 5$; $x^3 + 3x^2a + (3a^2 + 1)x + a^3 + a$.
16. $u^3 + 9u^2 + 27u + 23$. **18.** $x = 3, y = 0$; $x = -1, y = 4$.
19. $a^{\frac{3}{5}}$; $a^{\frac{9}{2}}$; $a^{\frac{5}{6}}$; $a^{\frac{3}{4}}$; $a^{\frac{23}{8}}$; $a^{\frac{3}{15}}$. **20.** First, second, third, fifth, seventh.
21. 1; 10; 2; 16; $\frac{1}{3}$; 3; 1. **22.** 4. **23.** 1.86570; 2.86570; 7.95231 $-$ 10;
0.95231; 506.8; 0.3234; 57.24. **24.** 2.4; 1.5; -0.375; -0.857. **25.** 6;
3; 1; 0.5; 1; -2; 2; 0. **26.** $x = 3.544$; $\log_5 300 = 3.544$. **27.** $v = a^u$;
$v = 10^{-5u}$; $v = u^3$. **28.** $p = q/(q - 1)$. **29.** Neither; geometric;
neither; arithmetic; arithmetic; geometric; geometric; neither. **30.** 2;
$\frac{2}{3}$. **31.** 2500. **32.** 1.6 meters; 117 meters; 135 meters. **33.** 3.
34. $\frac{7}{24}$. **35.** No. It provides the ratio d/c. **36.** $-6(i + 1)$.
37. $-3i$; -1; -5; i. **38.** $\sqrt{-i} = (1 - i)/\sqrt{2}$. **39.** $y = 13.5$;
$k = \frac{1}{2}$. **40.** 2.2 minutes.

CHAPTER 3

2. $k = 11$. **3.** $y = 3x + 5$; $y = (\frac{1}{2})x + 2$; $y = 2x + 1$; $y = x - 2$;
$y = -2x + 2$; $y = x + 1$; $y = -4x + 13$. **4.** Rectangle.
5. $y' = -2x'$; $y' = 2x' - 1$; $y' = 0.06x'$. **6.** $x'^2 + y'^2 = 36$;
$x'^2 + y'^2 = 36$; $x'^2 + y'^2 = 36$; $x'^2 + 8x' + y'^2 + 6y' = 11$.
7. $x'^2 - y'^2 = 32$. **8.** s vs. $1/t$. s vs. $\log_{10} t$. Yes. Yes, since a straight
line can be more accurately plotted than any other curve.

CHAPTER 4

1. $7\pi/4$; π; π; 0.8π; 0; $2\pi - 1 = 5.28$; $2\pi - 4.8 = 1.48$; 0.5π.   **2.** $\pi/18$; 1; $3\pi/4$; $7\pi/6$; $4\pi/3$; $3\pi/2$; $5\pi/3$; $35\pi/18$.   **3.** $57°$; $171°$; $240°$; $225°$; $270°$; $157.5°$; $315°$; $540°$.   **4.** $\pi/12$ meters.   **5.** $\sqrt{3}/2$; $\sqrt{2}/2$; 0; 0; -1; -0.5; $-\sqrt{3}/2$; 0.5; $-\sqrt{3}/2$; $-\sqrt{2}/2$; $\sqrt{2}/2$.   **6.** 0.46 rad.

CHAPTER 5

1. (a) $\frac{26}{3}$.   **2.** (a) 4 and 20.   **3.** (a) $\frac{52}{3}$; $\frac{86}{3}$.   **4.** $+$; $+$; $-$; $-$; $-$; $+$.
5. (a) 6; (b) 18; (c) $\frac{1}{2}$.   **6.** 4; $\frac{3}{4}$; $-\frac{5}{6}$; 8; $\frac{19}{3}$; $\frac{1}{2}$; 0.
7. $(\frac{7}{2})s^2 - 5s - s^3/3 - \frac{11}{6}$; $4a^3/3$.   **8.** $\frac{11}{6}$.   **9.** 0; $\frac{2}{3}$; 0; 0.   **10.** $-\frac{2}{3}$; 2; $\frac{8}{3}$; $-68\frac{4}{15}$.   **11.** $\frac{32}{3}$.

CHAPTER 6

1. $dy/dx = 6x^2 - 2x + 6$; $dy/dx = 2 + 28x + 51x^2 + 48x^3$; $dy/dx = 6 + 39x^2 - 28x^3$.   **2.** $dx/dy = 2y - 5$; $dt/ds = 6s$.
3. $dQ/dT = b + 2cT + 3dT^2$.   **4.** $dy/dx = -10/x^{11}$;
$dy/dx = -6/x^3 - 4/x^2 - 1$; $dy/dx = 2/(x + 1)^2$;
$dy/dx = 4x^3 - 3x^2 + 4x - 2$; $du/dy = 3(16 + y^2)/(16 - y^2)^2$;
$ds/dt = t(t - 2)/(t - 1)^2$; $dy/dx = (x^2 - 8x + 4)/(x^2 - 4)^2$;
$dy/dx = -b/(a + bx)^2$; $dy/dx = mn(x^{n-1} - x^{m-1})$;
$dy/dx = [(n - 1)x^n + (n + 1)x^{-n}]/x^2$.   **5.** $(2, -15)$ and $(-2, 17)$.
8. $dy/dx = \log x + 1$; $dy/dx = (1 - \log x)/x^2$; $dy/dx = (3 - 2\log x)/x^3$.
9. $dr/d\theta = \cos^2 \theta - \sin^2 \theta$;
$dy/dx = -10(2\cos x - \sin x)/(\cos x + 2\sin x)^2$;
$dy/dx = -\sin x + \cos x$; $dy/dx = 2\cos x/(1 - \sin x)^2$;
$dy/dx = x^2 \cos x$; $dy/dx = x^2 \sin x$; $dy/dx = x\cos x$;
$dy/dx = -1/(1 - \cos x)$.   **10.** $1/\cos^2 x$; $-1/\sin^2 x$; $\sec x \tan x$; $-\operatorname{cosec} x \cot x$.   **11.** $dy/dx = (x\cos x - \sin x)/x^2$.
12. $dy/dx = -ce^{-cx}$; $dy/dx = e^x(x + 1)$; $dy/dx = e^{-x}(1 - x)$;
$dy/dx = xe^{-x}(2 - x)$; $dy/dx = -e^{-x}(\sin x + \cos x)$;
$dy/dx = (\frac{1}{2})(e^x - e^{-x})$; $dy/dx = 4/(e^x + e^{-x})^2$.   **13.** $da^x/dx = (\log a)a^x$.
14. Three times the area of a side $(dV/dl = 3l^2)$.

CHAPTER 7

4. $4x$; $x^2/4$; $x^2(\frac{1}{2} - x/3)$; $x^3 + 2x^2 - 5x$; $(x + 1)^3$; $-1/x$; $x + 2/x$.
5. $(\frac{3}{4})x^8 - 5x^2 + x$; $x^3/3 + 1/x$; $x + \log x - 1/x$; $2\sqrt{x} + (\frac{2}{3})x^{\frac{3}{2}}$.
6. $2; 1; 0; e - 1/e; 1 - \log 2; (\frac{1}{2})(e^2 - 1)$. **8.** 1. **9.** $\log x; 1 - \cos t$;
$\sin t$. **10.** $-dc/dt = kc; c = c_0 e^{-kt}$. **11.** $N = N_0 e^{kt}$.

CHAPTER 8

1. $dy/dx = 1/(x \log x)$; $dy/dx = -2xe^{-x^2}$; $dy/dx = -2kxe^{-kx^2}$;
$dy/dx = x^x(1 + \log x)$. **2.** $dy/dx = \sin(x^2) + 2x^2 \cos(x^2)$;
$dy/dx = -6x \sin(3x^2 + 5)$; $dy/dx = \cot x$; $dy/dx = 1/(1 + x)$;
$dy/dx = 2x/(1 + x^2)$; $dy/dx = 1$. **4.** 9.95; 5.991; 2.32. **5.** $1 \pm (\frac{1}{2})\alpha$;
$1 \mp (\frac{1}{2})\alpha$. **7.** $(2/5b)(a + bx)^{\frac{5}{2}}$; impossible by change of variable;
$(\frac{1}{2}) \sin (x^2)$; $\log (1 + x)$; $(\frac{1}{3}) \log (2 + 3x)$; $-(\frac{1}{3})(1 - 2x)^{\frac{3}{2}}$;
impossible by change of variable; $(\frac{1}{2})e^{x^2}$. **8.** $-\frac{2}{9}$; $(\frac{1}{8})(1 - e^{-64})$.
10. $f'(x) = -3/x^4, f''(x) = 12/x^5; f'(x) = 2x \cos (x^2)$,
$f''(x) = 2 \cos (x^2) - 4x^2 \sin (x^2); f'(x) = 2/(x + 1)^2$,
$f''(x) = -4/(x + 1)^3; f'(x) = -3 \sin 3x, f''(x) = -9 \cos 3x$;
$f'(x) = x \cos x, f''(x) = \cos x - x \sin x; f'(x) = 3e^{3x}, f''(x) = 9e^{3x}$.
12. $x = \pm(2n + 1)\pi/2$, $n = 0, 1, 2, \ldots$, and $y = \pm 1$ alternately;
$x = \pm n\pi$, $n = 0, 1, 2, \ldots$, and $y = \pm 1$ alternately; $(0,0)$ and points
having $x = \pm \sqrt{(2n + 1)\pi/2}$, $n = 0, 1, 2, \ldots$, and $y = \pm 1$ alternately, except that $y = +1$ at $x = \pm \sqrt{\pi/2}$. **13.** $x = \pm\pi/6, \pm 5\pi/6$,
$\pm 7\pi/6, \pm 11\pi/6, \pm 13\pi/6, \ldots$; $x = (\frac{1}{2}) \log 2$; $x = 0, x = -2$, and
$x = -\infty$. **16.** $(\partial T/\partial V)_p = p/a$; $(\partial T/\partial p)_V = V/a$;
$dT = (p/a) \, dV + (V/a) \, dp$; $(\partial p/\partial V)_T = -aT/V^2$; $(\partial p/\partial T)_V = a/V$;
$(\partial V/\partial T)_p = a/p$. **17.** $(\partial f/\partial x)_y = y$; $(\partial f/\partial y)_x = x$; $(\partial^2 f/\partial x^2)_y = 0$;
$(\partial^2 f/\partial y^2)_x = 0$; $(\partial^2 f/\partial x \partial y) = 1$; $(\partial^2 f/\partial y \partial x) = 1$.
18. $f_x = -x(x^2 + y^2 + z^2)^{-\frac{3}{2}}, f_y = -y(x^2 + y^2 + z^2)^{-\frac{3}{2}}$,
$f_z = -z(x^2 + y^2 + z^2)^{-\frac{3}{2}}$.

CHAPTER 9

1. $5\hat{\imath} + 20\hat{\jmath} - 10\hat{k}$; $9\hat{\imath} + 35\hat{\jmath} - 10\hat{k}$; $\hat{\imath} + 20\hat{\jmath} - 20\hat{k}$;
$-5\hat{\imath} + 13\hat{\jmath} - 6\hat{k}$.   6. $m = -n$, $m\mathbf{A} = -n\mathbf{B} \to \mathbf{A} = \mathbf{B}$.   8. They form
a 3, 4, 5 right triangle.   9. $1/\sqrt{2}, 1/\sqrt{2}$.   10. $\hat{\imath}' = \cos\theta\,\hat{\imath} + \sin\theta\,\hat{\jmath}$;
$\hat{\jmath}' = -\sin\theta\,\hat{\imath} + \cos\theta\,\hat{\jmath}$.   11. $\mathbf{A} = (A/B)\mathbf{B} \to \mathbf{A}\|\mathbf{B}$.   12. $(\frac{1}{2})(\mathbf{A} + \mathbf{B})$.
13. The vector is $2\hat{\imath} - 3\hat{\jmath}$ and has no z-component.   Its magnitude is
$\sqrt{13}$.   14. Ratio of lengths is $1:3$.

CHAPTER 10

1. -69; 634; $100\hat{\imath} - 45\hat{\jmath} - 40\hat{k}$, 267; 0; $70\hat{\imath} - 60\hat{\jmath} - 85\hat{k}$; 285.
2. $\mathbf{A} \cdot \mathbf{B} = \cos(\theta - \phi)$, $\mathbf{A} \times \mathbf{B} = \sin(\phi - \theta)\hat{k}$, etc.   3. -1.2.
4. $x = 4$.

CHAPTER 11

1. A; $A\omega(-\sin\omega t\,\hat{\imath} + \cos\omega t\,\hat{\jmath})$; $A\omega$; $-A\omega^2(\cos\omega t\,\hat{\imath} + \sin\omega t\,\hat{\jmath}) = -\omega^2\mathbf{r}$;
0; 0.

GLOSSARY
OF SYMBOLS
AND STANDARD
ABBREVIATIONS

A	Area
dx	An infinitesimal change in x; an infinitesimal interval on the x-axis
dy/dx	The derivative of y with respect to x
d^2y/dx^2	The second derivative of y with respect to x
$(\partial f/\partial x)_y,\ \ldots$	The partial derivative of $f(x,y,\ \ldots)$ with respect to x
e	The base of the natural logarithms
$f(x),\ g(x),\ \ldots$	Functions of the variable x
$f'(x)$	The derivative of $f(x)$ with respect to x
$f''(x)$	The second derivative of $f(x)$ with respect to x
f_x	The partial derivative of $f(x,y,\ \ldots)$ with respect to x
i	The imaginary unit, $\sqrt{-1}$
$\lim_{a \to b}$	The limit, as a approaches b
$\log_a b$	The logarithm of b to the base a
$\log b$	The logarithm of b to the base e
m	The slope of a line
p	The perimeter of a two-dimensional closed figure
rad	Radians (angle measure)

V	Volume
Δx	A finite change in x; a finite interval on the x-axis
$\cong$	Is congruent to
$\sim$	Is similar to
$\perp$	Is perpendicular to
$\equiv$	Is identical to; is defined as
$>$	Is greater than
$<$	Is less than
$\displaystyle\sum_{j=n}^{N}$	The sum of terms obtained by letting j take on all integral values between n and N
$\lvert n \rvert$	The absolute value of n
c^{*}	The complex conjugate (c.c.) of c
$\propto$	Is proportional to
$\rightarrow$	Approaches; implies
∞	An infinitely large number ("infinity")
$^{\circ}$	Degrees (angle measure)
$\int$	The indefinite integral
$\displaystyle\int_{a}^{b}$	The definite integral from a to b
$f(x)\Big\vert_{a}^{b}$	$f(b) - f(a)$
$\hat{\mathbf{n}}$	The unit vector in the direction of $\mathbf{n}$
$\parallel$	Is parallel to
anti-$\parallel$	Is antiparallel to (i.e., along the same direction, but pointing in the opposite sense)
$\hat{\mathbf{i}},\ \hat{\mathbf{j}},\ \hat{\mathbf{k}}$	Unit vectors along the x, y, z axes, respectively
$\mathbf{A}\cdot\mathbf{B}$	The scalar product of $\mathbf{A}$ and $\mathbf{B}$
$\mathbf{A}\times\mathbf{B}$	The vector product of $\mathbf{A}$ and $\mathbf{B}$

INDEX